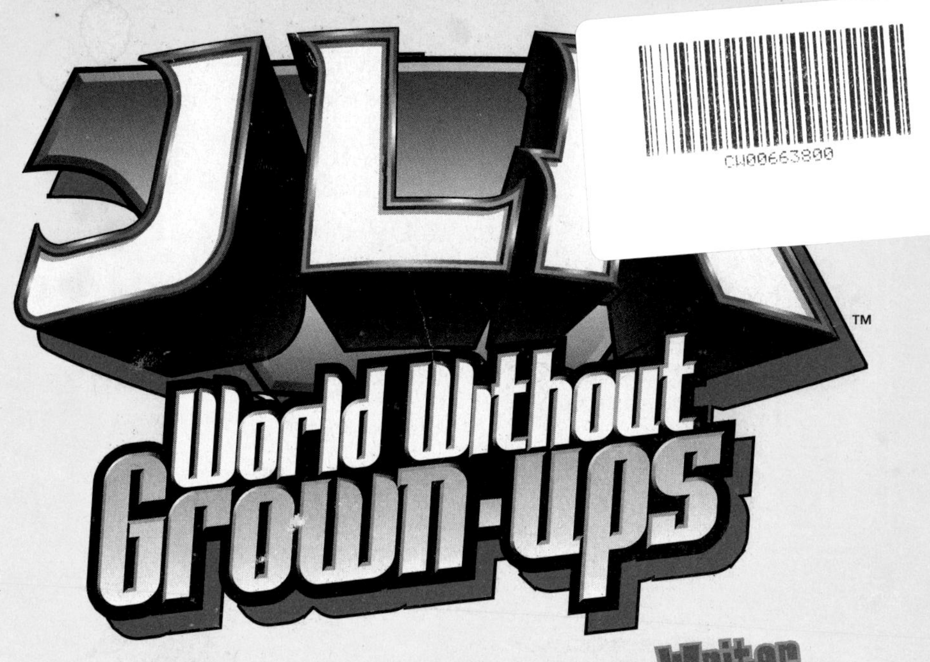




featuring
- ROBIN
- SUPERBOY
- IMPULSE

Todd Dezago **Writer**

Todd Nauck **Pencillers**
Humberto Ramos
Mike McKone

Lary Stucker **Inkers**
Wayne Faucher
Paul Neary
Mark McKenna

Jason Wright **Colorist**

Ken Lopez **Letterers**
John Workman

Special thanks to
Grant Morrison

As Batman's junior partner, Tim Drake has undergone grueling training to become a formidable martial artist and detective, helping to defend Gotham City from a host of psychopaths and criminals. Tim knows full well that being Robin isn't always the most sensible decision, but it is one fueled by an ethical code and sense of responsibility that won't allow him to quit.

A clone created to replace Superman, Superboy is in fact a hybrid of human and Kryptonian DNA, a genetic mix that grants him both the power of "tactile telekinesis" — which duplicates several of his namesake's abilities — and a vulnerability to Kryptonite. Birthed before he had fully grown to adulthood, the headstrong Superboy may never mature beyond age sixteen.

Reared inside a Virtual Reality chamber in the 30th century, Bart Allen is the grandson of the late Barry Allen, the second super-speedster known as the Flash. But unlike his coolly rational grandfather, the attention-deficient Impulse goes from thought to deed in a single electric leap...too often without considering the consequences.

They are Earth's greatest heroes, guarding the planet from their lunar Watchtower as its first and last line of defense: **Superman**, the Man of Steel; **Batman**, the Dark Knight; the **Flash**, the Fastest Man Alive; **Wonder Woman**, the Amazing Amazon; **Aquaman**, King of the Seven Seas; J'onn J'onzz, the **Martian Manhunter**; **Green Lantern**, the Emerald Gladiator; **Zauriel**, an Earthbound Guardian Angel; **Plastic Man**, the Pliable Prankster; **Steel**, the Master Forger; and **Big Barda**, the Female Fury.

Impulse's mentor, the "Zen Master of Speed" has found his greatest challenge in teaching Bart how to slow down and live a "normal" life. Max would gladly trade this responsibility for season tickets to see the Atlanta Braves play ball. Any takers?

By uttering the name of the wizard Shazam, Billy is transformed by a mystic thunderbolt into Captain Marvel, the World's Mightiest Mortal, a champion imbued with the wisdom of Solomon, the strength of Hercules, the stamina of Atlas, the power of Zeus, the courage of Achilles, and the speed of Mercury. Despite these awesome abilities, Billy is still just a boy in a man's body.

GOOD JOB, ROBIN. YOU'VE MANAGED TO ANGER ALL THE WRONG PEOPLE.
I'M SURE THEY'VE TOLD YOU HOW... SERIOUS... THIS SITUATION IS. THOUSANDS OF LIVES WERE IN JEOPARDY AND YOU AND YOUR "FRIENDS" WERE RIGHT IN THE MIDDLE OF IT.
WE WANT YOUR SIDE OF THE STORY-- EVERY DETAIL!
TELL ME.
UM... WELL...
...OKAY...
AS FAR AS I CAN TELL, I BECAME INVOLVED THE NIGHT BEFORE--
--WHEN I GOT CURIOUS ABOUT THE MILITARY CONVOY THAT WAS SLINKING THROUGH GOTHAM IN THE MIDDLE OF THE NIGHT!
ROBIN
SUPERBOY
IMPULSE
YOUNG JUSTICE
THE
SECRET
WRITER-TODD DEZAGO
PENCILS-TODD NAUCK
INKS-LARY STUCKER
COLORS-JASON WRIGHT
SEPS-DIGITAL CHAMELEON
LETTERS-KEN LOPEZ
ASSOC. EDITOR-DANA KURTIN
EDITOR-EDDIE BERGANZA

BUT IT WASN'T UNTIL THE NEXT NIGHT, I HEARD ABOUT THE EVACUATION ON THE NEWS, AND DECIDED TO TAKE A DRIVE UPSTATE... I THOUGHT I MIGHT DO A LITTLE CHECKING AROUND ON MY OWN...!
AT LEAST THAT WAS MY PLAN...
YO! WONDER BOY!
SUPERBOY AND IMPULSE?!
WHAT ARE YOU GUYS DOING HERE?!
ARE YOU KIDDING?! THIS THING'S ALL OVER TV!
I SAW IT ON CNN.
MTV NEWS.
WHAT?
YOU HEAR IT... FIRST.
UNFORTUNATELY, MY 'FRIENDS' ARRIVAL WASN'T SO DISCREET, AND WE WERE SOON SURROUNDED BY A LESS-THAN-FRIENDLY WELCOMING COMMITTEE OF U.S. ARMY AND DEO* SECURITY GUYS--
KNOWING THE DEO HAS NO LOVE FOR SUPER-POWERED ANYBODY, WE TENTATIVELY OFFERED OUR HELP--
* THE DEPARTMENT OF EXTRANORMAL OPERATIONS--ED.

--AND WHILE THE MILITARY WAS RELUCTANT TO EVEN THINK ABOUT CUTTING US IN, I GUESS THE DEO GUY, A DR. CHARLES, WAS IN CHARGE, 'CAUSE HE TOLD US HE'D APPRECIATE ANY HELP WE COULD OFFER.
MUCH AS IT PAINS ME TO ADMIT IT, WE REALLY HAVE NO OTHER ALTERNATIVE. IF THE SUBJECT ISN'T RECAPTURED AND CONTAINED SOON...
...WE COULD BE RESPONSIBLE FOR A GREAT MANY DEATHS!
HE WENT ON TO FILL US IN ON... THE SUBJECT...
WE WERE IN THE PROCESS OF TRANSFERRING A HIGHLY VOLATILE CREATURE THAT WE'VE HAD IN OUR CHARGE FOR A NUMBER OF YEARS FROM OUR DOWNSTATE LOCATION TO OUR WABE FACILITY HERE IN THE ADIRONDACKS.
A HIGHLY DANGEROUS ENTITY, THE SUBJECT EXISTS IN A CONTINUOUS GASEOUS STATE, AND IS CAPABLE OF ALTERING ITS OWN TOXICITY, TO KILL AT A WHIM.
"DURING THE TRANSFER, A MISHAP OCCURRED, ALLOWING THE SMALLEST OF FISSURES IN THE SUBJECT'S CONTAINMENT UNIT-- SHE WAS FREE!
"SEVERAL MEN WERE KILLED--
"--IT ESCAPED INTO THE WILDERNESS."
HE TOLD US THAT THEY EVACUATED THE NEIGHBORING TOWN WITH A HAZMAT COVER STORY TO AVOID PANIC.
HE SAID THAT THE CREATURE WAS MORE DEADLY THAN ANY DISEASE-- MORE LETHAL THAN ANY VIRUS...
...AND ANGRY.

THEN WHAT?
THEN WE ASKED IF THEY'D LET US TAKE A CRACK AT IT... WHICH HAD THE HEAD ARMY GUY, LUTWIDGE, TOTALLY BUGGIN' OUT!...
EVENTUALLY DR. CHARLES TALKED HIM INTO LETTING US TRY.
LUTWIDGE RELUCTANTLY GAVE US TWO HOURS. HE SAID THAT WAS 'MAX,' THAT HE'D BE CALLING IN AN AIR STRIKE WHETHER WE WERE OUT OF THERE OR NOT!
HE WAS REALLY FRUSTRATED, AND RESENTED THE HECK OUT OF US FOR GOING IN TO DO THE JOB HE COULDN'T...!
THEY GAVE US THIS RADAR-LOCATER-THINGIE, AND THEN THEY ALL JUST GLARED AT US AS WE HEADED INTO THE DESERTED TOWN.
IT WAS SO QUIET... EVEN EMPTIER THAN A SHOWING OF THE POSTMAN.'
I'M GETTING NOTHING.
Y'KNOW, I COULD CANVASS THE WHOLE AREA IN A COUPLE OF SECONDS. SCARE THE THING UP, THEN WE'D KNOW WHERE IT IS!
AND THEN WHAT?
UM...
WELL...
...I DUNNO.

SEE, THAT'S JUST IT... WE'VE GOT TO HAVE A PLAN. AND WE'VE GOT TO BE READY FOR EVERYTHING!
IF WE JUST SCARE IT OUT, IT'S OUT! WE HAVE TO DRAW IT OUT, AND KEEP CONTROL OF THE SITUATION. WE HAVE TO KNOW WHAT WE'RE GOING TO DO NEXT AND WE HAVE TO WORK TOGETHER... LIKE A TEAM...
THAT'S WHAT THE JUSTICE LEAGUE DOES...
SO I VOLUNTEERED TO DO A LITTLE SUBTLE SCOPING AROUND, A QUIET FLY-OVER TO GET THE LAY OF THE LAND...
SUPERBOY--WE'RE GOING TO NEED YOU TO RUN A LITTLE RECON MISSION. JUST GO--
HEY, WAIT A MINUTE! WHO DIED AND MADE YOU LEX LUTHOR?! YOU'RE NOT THE BOSS OF ME! WHY DO I--
DUH...? MAYBE BECAUSE YOU'RE THE ONLY ONE WHO CAN FLY..?
LOOK, YOU KNOW YOU HAVE TO DO IT... THIS REQUIRES A LITTLE STEALTH, SO THAT RULES OUT THE TASMANIAN DEVIL HERE. YOU'RE THE ONLY ONE WHO CAN DO THIS, SO LET'S NOT ARGUE JUST TO ARGUE, OKAY?
...
...OKAY.

OKAY. NOW, LISTEN-- IMPULSE. I NEED YOU TO GO TO THE DEO COMPOUND AND--
GOTCHA.

ZWIP

AND... UM...
...WHAT?

IT WAS TOUGH, BUT ROBIN FINALLY GOT IMPULSE TO CHILL LONG ENOUGH TO LISTEN TO WHAT WE WERE GONNA NEED!
Y'KNOW, WHEN AND IF WE EVER GET TO BE THE JUSTICE LEAGUE-- I DON'T KNOW WHETHER WE'LL BE THAT KID'S TEAMMATES--
--OR HIS PARENTS!

OH, YEAH? WELL, THEN I KNOW WHICH ONE YOU'RE GONNA BE...
OH, NO! IT'S NOT ME! I'M NOT THE MOM!
I AM NOT THE MOM!!

...SO THEY SENT ME BACK TO THE COMPOUND TO PICK UP A CONTAINMENT CANISTER, AND BLAH BLAH BLAH, YADDA YADDA YADDA, ARE WE ALMOST DONE HERE? CAUSE I'M REALLY--
SIT UP!
SHWOOOP

I DON'T THINK I NEED TO IMPRESS UPON YOU THE SEVERITY OF THIS SITUATION.
THERE ARE A LOT OF IMPORTANT PEOPLE WHO HAVE CONCERNS REGARDING THIS MATTER-- THERE ARE QUESTIONS THAT NEED TO BE ADDRESSED.
NOW CONTINUE WITH YOUR STORY...
W-WELL... UM...
...SO THEY SENT ME FOR A CONTAINMENT UNIT...

ZWIP
...ANOTHER DEFECTIVE CANISTER?!? PUT IT OVER WITH THE OTHER ONES AND BE SURE THAT IT'S PROPERLY LABELLED! DAMNED 'O' RINGS!
AND SEE TO IT THAT OUR LITTLE "ACCIDENT" IS IN PLACE. IF THOSE THREE PUNKS COME THROUGH, I'M NOT GOING TO RUN THE RISK OF THAT...THING GETTING OUT AGAIN!

YES, SIR, I'LL--
HEY! WHERE'D IT--
SWIPE

...WHICH TOOK ME ALL OF ABOUT 5 SECONDS.
THERE YOU GO. NOW WHAT?

OKAY, WONDER--I GOT THE PERFECT SPOT ALL PICKED OUT...
THIS IS EXCELLENT, JUST WHAT WE NEED.
Y'KNOW, I COULDA JUST RUN UP HERE...
NOT YET.
GAS
S-BOY TOOK US UP ON A CLIFF OVERLOOKING THE TOWN, AND THEN ROBIN FINALLY TOLD US WHAT HE WAS PLANNING TO DO...
...HE TOOK FOREVER EXPLAINING IT...

...BUT EVENTUALLY WE WERE READY TO GO.
OKAY? EVERYBODY KNOWS WHAT THEY'RE S'POSED TO DO...?
NOW?
OKAY, SPEEDY-- IT'S GO TIME!
THAT WAS MY PART OF THE JOB--
--TO BEAT THE BUSHES--
--TO CANVASS THE TOWN AND THE SURROUNDING WOODS AT LIGHTNING SPEED!
"AS FAST AS I COULD," ROBIN SAID--
--"LEAVE NO STONE UNTURNED"--
--WHICH WAS ACTUALLY KINDA FUNNY...

...CONSIDERING WHERE IT ALL ENDED UP!
RVO
FORRESTER
ROBI
MST
SHROOOARRR!
YIKES!
SUDDENLY, IT WAS ALL AROUND ME! AND IT WAS BIG!
AND SMOKY!
AND MAD!

THERE IT IS. GET US THERE...
...FAST.
DON'T BLINK.
BART--YOU OKAY?
FINE.
READY?

LET'S DO IT!
ROBIN HAD IT FIGURED OUT PERFECTLY--
--IT COULDN'T GO WRONG!

I WASN'T TOTALLY SURE THAT IT WAS GOING TO WORK. I JUST KEPT HOPING WE WERE USING OUR RESOURCES TO THE BEST ADVANTAGE...
SHOOOAAR!
...IMPULSE SAID THAT HE'D BE MOVING TOO FAST TO WORRY ABOUT THE POISON GASES OF THE THING. AND SUPERBOY...
...WELL, HE SAYS HE'S INVULNERABLE TO EVERYTHING!
HE BRACED HIMSELF AND THE CANISTER WITH HIS TACTILE TELEKINESIS AND WAS ABLE TO STAND IN THE CENTER OF THE INCREDIBLE VORTEX IMPULSE WHIPPED UP--
SHOOOARRR?!
--AND BEFORE THE... SUBJECT EVEN KNEW WHAT WAS GOING ON--
--IT WAS OVER.
GOTCHA.
HEY! WE DID IT! WE'RE TALKIN' REAL TEAMWORK! WE--
--HUH?!?

SO YOU WERE ABLE TO CONTAIN THE... SUBJECT WITHOUT INCIDENT?
YEAH, UM...
...YES.

NONE OF YOU WERE AFFECTED IN ANY WAY BY THE SUBJECT'S TOXICITY?
NO.

DID YOU NOTICE ANYTHING... STRANGE ABOUT THE SUBJECT ONCE YOU HAD IT CAPTURED...?
UH... NO.

--YOU GUYS! THIS IS LIKE TOTALLY WHACKED!
I MEAN, IS IT ME--
--OR DOES THAT LOOK LIKE A GIRL IN THERE?!

SHE'S OUT!
I'm SORRY... But, THANK YOU--
--I KNEW you'd help...
YOU WERE ABLE TO GET OUT ALL ALONG, WEREN'T YOU?
BAILEY
CRIT
1899-1966
THEN WHY DIDN'T YOU...?
I...I wanted you to BELIEVE me... to...TRUST me.
I need your HELP. I need...
...some FRIENDS.

I'm sorry that I tried to SCARE YOU before, I just... didn't know WHAT to do... I was scared...!
When you turn me over to DR. CHARLES, he plans to "silence" me. He'll SAY that he's mixing me with oxygen to CALM ME DOWN--
--but it'll REALLY be potassium chloride... which will r-render me...
...inert.
INERT...?!
SHE MEANS DEAD, DOOFUS!
and I...
...I can't...
--ahuh--huh--
NICE JOB, DOOFUS!
SHUT UP!
NO! YOU!
HEY, TAKE IT EASY... WE'RE NUH--
?!

AND SO, YOU SIMPLY CAPTURED THE "SUBJECT" AND PROMPTLY HANDED THE CYLINDER OVER?
SURE.
AN EXCELLENT JOB, BOYS--WE CAN'T THANK YOU ENOUGH!
IT CHECKS OUT, SIR. IT'S HE-...ER, IT'S THE "SUBJECT."
DEEDEET DEET DEET

OKAY, TROOPS--LET'S MOVE! WE DON'T WANT ANY MORE SLIP-UPS! LET'S
WHY DON'T WE MOVE OUT OF THEIR WAY, BOYS. GIVE THEM ROOM TO WORK.
WHAT ARE THEY DOING?

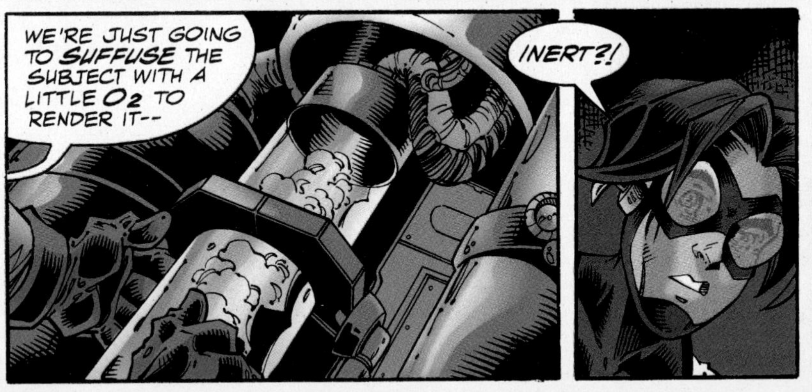
WE'RE JUST GOING TO SUFFUSE THE SUBJECT WITH A LITTLE O2 TO RENDER IT--
INERT?!

HEH-HEH--NO, SON. UNCONSCIOUS.
THE OXYGEN WILL ACT AS A SEDATIVE.

AND SO WE JUST WATCHED WHEN THE MACHINE STARTED PUMPING IN THE...
...OXYGEN...
SSSSSS
AND THEN--
WHOOM
WHAT WAS THAT HAPPENED?!
I-I, ER... I DON'T KNOW!--
POSSIBLY THE UH... OXYGEN MIXTURE WAS TOO RICH...? A-A SHORT IN THE SYSTEM...? I...

AND THAT'S HOW IT HAPPENED.
...TRAGIC. TRULY TRAGIC...

AND THIS... "SUBJECT... IS THERE ANY CHANCE THAT IT SURVIVED..?
SMOKE CAPSULES--DON'T LEAVE THE BATCAVE WITHOUT 'EM...!
I THINK IT'S COOL NOW. LET HER OUT.
NELSON 1903-1972
Oh, thankyou-thankyouthankyou-thankyouthankyou-thankyou!
You guys are WONDERFUL!! You're the BEST!!
Oh, I'm FREE!! I can't WAIT!!

I've never had FREEDOM before...!!
I can't WAIT to go and find out what the WORLD is like...!!
THANK you, THANK you SO MUCH!!
HEY, WAIT! BEFORE YOU GO--
--WHAT'S YOUR NAME?
Y'know-- I think I'm going to go and find out what THAT is, too!!
Thank you again! I'm Freeeeee!
SHE CAN ONLY STAY FREE IF SHE STAYS "DEAD". THIS GOES NO FURTHER, YOU GUYS. WE KEEP IT AMONG OURSELVES...
A SECRET.
WELL, I GUESS--
--THAT IT WAS KILLED--
--IN THE EXPLOSION.

WE'RE AGREED THEN? WE TELL THE DEO THAT THE GUYS HAVE BEEN DEBRIEFED AND THAT THEIR CONCERNS ARE UNFOUNDED.
THE DEO SEEMS VERY FOCUSED ON THAT POINT--SHOULD WE BE SUS-PICIOUS?
THE BOYS DIDN'T. I TRUST THEM...
...WELL... I TRUST ROBIN AND SUPERBOY...
I'M SATISFIED.
THEIR STORIES DO MATCH...
BATMAN...?
I DON'T TRUST THE DEO. I'VE DEALT WITH THEM BEFORE. THEIR METHODS LEAVE MUCH TO BE DESIRED.
--THAT THE BOYS' STORIES CHECK OUT AND THAT THEY EACH BELIEVE THAT THE "SUBJECT'S" DEATH WAS COMPLETELY ACCIDENTAL--THAT THE DEO COULD IN NO WAY BE HELD RESPONSIBLE FOR IT...
THEY'RE GOOD KIDS. THEY CERTAINLY KNOW RIGHT FROM WRONG. WHATEVER HAPPENED, I'M SURE THEY DID THE RIGHT THING...
AND IF, FOR SOME REASON, THEY COULDN'T TELL US THE ENTIRE TRUTH, WELL...
...WE ALL HAVE OUR... LITTLE SECRETS...
...DON'T WE?
KLIK

JLA
World Without
Grown-Ups

"HE'S GOOD. I'LL GIVE HIM THAT...
"...VERY GOOD.
"DIFFICULT TO TRAIL... HE HAS ABOUT TWENTY MINUTES ON ME.
"I'VE FOLLOWED HIM TO THE OUT-SKIRTS OF GOTHAM...
"...EAST--HERE, TO THE SOUTHERN EDGE OF THE HARBOR...
KRAKAA KOOM
"...THE ABANDONED TRAIN YARDS...

"DESOLATE. HARD.

"FOLLOWING IN HIS TRACKS.

"HE'S CLEVER.

"A PREDATOR RARELY TAKES THE TIME TO COVER HIS TRAIL.

"HE'S A SKILLED FIGHTER--
"--THINKING AS HE STRIKES--
"--TRAINED TO USE HIS SIZE TO HIS ADVANTAGE...

"--TO MAXIMIZE HIS POWER--
KOOM
GLORSH
"--AND TO USE HIS OPPONENT'S POWER AGAINST HIM!
"HIS MOVEMENTS ARE GRACEFUL--"
ERSSH!
"--FLUID.
"--BUT NOT FLAWLESS.
"A SLIP ON THE OIL AND IT'S SUDDENLY SERIOUS.
"AND JUST AS SUDDENLY, I'M MET WITH AN IMAGE THAT STABS AT MY MEMORY AND MAKES MY BLOOD RUN COLD...
"...A VISION OF UNBEARABLE PAIN...
"...BANE.
"BUT I EXIST ON 'SUDDENLY'S,' AND ABANDON THE ROLE OF OBSERVER--

"THE MOMENT OF FEAR HAS TRANSFORMED ME INTO HIS PROTECTOR"...
CHUD
"...GUARDIAN."
UNGH!
KRAKA
I WAS WATCHING.
ARE YOU ALL RIGHT?
I'LL GET HIM. GO BACK TO THE CAVE.
BUT I'M FINE. I RODE THIS GUY THIS FAR, AND I--
BATMAN!? I...
...YEAH, I'M GOOD TO GO. LET'S GET THIS GUY. I--
ROBIN.
"HE WOULDN'T UNDERSTAND...
OH, MAN...

...DOWNTOWN METROPOLIS, WHERE CENTENNIAL PARK HAS BEEN TURNED INTO A VERITABLE BATTLEGROUND--
--WITH THE SUDDEN APPEARANCE OF A STORIES-TALL GIANT SAMURAI ROBOT BENT ON DUKING IT OUT WITH THE MAN OF STEEL!
FORTUNATELY, THE ROBOT'S RAMPAGE IS BEING QUICKLY QUELLED BY THE EQUALLY SUDDEN ARRIVAL OF THE KID HIMSELF--
--SUPERBOY!
SUPERMAN...
NO, JOLLY TIN GIANT! SUPERBOY!--BOY!
THIS GIANT ROBO WANNABE WAS SENT TO THROW DOWN WITH SUPES? IT'S WEAK! I'VE ONLY BEEN HERE TWO MINUTES, AND I'VE ALREADY GOT THIS THING TOTTERING--
MBC

ONE LAST "TWISKER" PUNCH, AND IT'S--
WHOA! PLAYERS ON THE FIELD!?!
HOW'D THEY SLIP PAST THE POLICE BARRI--
SWAT
SUPERMAN...
SHKK
SO, YOU WANNA MESS WITH THE KID?!
TELL YOU WHAT--
...SUPERMAN...?
...I'LL BE THE KID...
...YOU BE THE MESS!
KRAWHAWW

SUPER-BOY! SUPER-BOY!
SUPERBOY, THAT WAS MAGNIFICENT! TELL US, WHAT ARE YOU DOING IN METROPOLIS?
THANKS! THANKS! ACTUALLY, I WAS JUST PASSING THROUGH, KINDA RUNNING A SUPER-ERRAND FOR PROJECT CADMUS--
--WHEN I SAW THAT THING STOMPIN' AROUND! GUESS IT WAS LOOKIN' TO TUSSLE WITH THE "BIG S"--
BUT TURNS OUT IT COULDN'T EVEN KICK A LITTLE "S"!
WELL...GOTTA BOAT, THANKS FOR THE GRATITUDE...IT WAS MY PLEASURE!
BUT...
YOUNG MAN, YOU DON'T INTEND TO SIMPLY FLY AWAY, DO YOU?
HUH?
LOOK AT THE DAMAGE CAUSED BY YOUR LITTLE TESTOSTERONE-DRIVEN TETE-A-TETE WITH THAT AUTOMATON! AREN'T YOU GOING TO ASSIST WITH THE CLEARING OF THE DEBRIS?
LUTHOR?!
WHAT ARE YOU DOING HERE?
I SHOULD BE ASKING THAT OF YOU.
IF YOU MUST KNOW, I WAS JUST PICKING UP A LITTLE TRINKET FOR MY DAUGHTER LENA.

LOOK, LUTHOR-- I KNOW HOW YOU LIKE TO MANIPULATE PEOPLE TO YOUR OWN ENDS...
BUT I JUST SAVED THIS ENTIRE CITY FROM THAT THING, AND I'M NOT GONNA START JUMPING THROUGH YOUR HOOPS!
SO... SEE YA...
HUH?
SUPERMAN?!
SORRY, SUPERBOY.
AS BAD A TASTE AS IT LEAVES IN YOUR MOUTH, LUTHOR'S RIGHT. AS HEROES, WE'RE OBLIGATED TO SET A GOOD EXAMPLE. DO THE RIGHT THING.
AND TAKE RESPONSI-BILITY FOR OUR ACTIONS.
C'MON, KID-- I'LL GIVE YOU A HAND.
OH, MAN...

MANCHESTER, ALABAMA...
AT THE QUIET SUBURBAN HOME OF HELEN CLAIBORNE--
--(ALSO THE CURRENT RESIDENCE OF ONE MAX MERCURY AND HIS YOUNG NOVICE BART ALLEN--
--AND THE VISITING CAROL TRENT, THE FRIEND WHO WOULDN'T LEAVE.)
--SHORTLY AFTER DINNER, JUST AROUND DUSK-- MORE SPECIFICALLY--
--HOMEWORK TIME!
HONESTLY, BART--
POP.
POP.
POP.
--YOU ARE THE ONLY PERSON I KNOW WHO COULD ACTUALLY BECOME IMPATIENT WITH A MICROWAVE!
POP.
POP.
SORRY, CAROL--BUT WHY DOES IT HAVE TO TAKE SO LONG TO POP?
POP.
POP.
POP.
POP.
POP.
AND SHORTLY...
LA LA LA, LA LA LA.
BART.
HUH ?!
OOPS.

DON'T WORRY-- I'LL GET IT.
KETCH
KETCH
KETCH
PLUK
KETCH
KETCH
PLUK
BART, YOU WERE SENT TO YOUR ROOM OVER AN HOUR AGO, AND YOU'VE EASILY BEEN OUT HERE TEN TIMES SINCE THEN...
NOW I WANT YOU TO STOP PROCRASTINATING, GET BACK IN THERE, AND FOCUS ON THAT HOMEWORK.
THEN YOU CAN PLAY WITH YOUR LITTLE FRIEND.
OKAY, OKAY.
AND REMEMBER: YOU'RE TO STUDY AT NORMAL SPEED! SLOW DOWN AND THINK! IT'S IMPORTANT THAT YOU LEARN HOW TO LEARN--
--YOU KNOW THAT THAT SPEED LEARNING DOESN'T STICK...
NOW GET TO WORK.

OH, AND ONE MORE THING-- I'LL BE--
--?!
WHERE...?
...GOAT-SUCKER?!...
THE BIG BOOK OF UNEXPLAINED
THE BIG BOOK OF THE UNEXPLAINED
"...PUERTO RICO?!"
RAOOOWR?!
C'MON OUT, LITTLE CHUPACAB--

--MAX?!
WHAT
ARE
YOU
DOING?
ULP!--I'M BACK IN MY ROOM...? ...DOING MY HOME-WORK...?
NOW.
--AND MAYBE, YOUNG MAN, YOU CAN LEARN TO SLOW DOWN AND THINK--
--AND BE MORE RESPONSIBLE WITH YOUR POWERS--
--WHILE YOU'RE GROUNDED THIS WEEKEND. NOW GET TO THAT HOMEWORK.
BART
OH, MAN...

THE STUART HOME--
--IN A SUBURB OUTSIDE OF BOSTON.
HAPPY BIRTHD
MATT
--DEAR MA-ATT, HAPPY BIRTHDAY TO YOU!
NOW, C'MON, MATTY-- BLOW OUT THE CANDLES!
OKAY, ALREADY ...BUT IT'S NOT EVEN LIKE A REAL BIRTHDAY! I MEAN, I'M TURNING THIRTEEN, AND DAD'S NOT EVEN--

I'M HOME!
DADDY!
DADDY!

MATTHEW...?! COME AND SAY HELLO TO YOUR FATHER!

MATT! HAPPY BIRTHDAY, BUDDY! I TOLDJA I'D MAKE IT!

YA ALMOST DIDN'T.

OH, SO I'M THE REASON FOR THE ATTITUDE ...?
WELL, I THINK I'VE GOT SOMETHING THAT QUALIFIES FOR A BIRTHDAY PRESENT RIGHT HERE THAT OUGHT TO TURN THAT MOOD AROUND!

WH- WHAT IS IT ...?
LOOKS COOL, HUH? WE FOUND IT IN THE DIG. PROFESSOR JONES BELIEVES THAT IT WAS THE TOY OF AN ATLANTEAN BOY ABOUT YOUR AGE, BUT WE COULDN'T FIGURE OUT JUST WHAT IT WAS!
I SAID THAT IF ANY-ONE COULD MAKE IT WORK, IT WOULD BE YOU!
WHAT DO YOU THINK?
IT'S FINE.
...BUT I WANTED A PLAYTENDO...
MATTHEW STUART! I'VE HAD ENOUGH OF THIS!
YOUR FATHER CAME BACK FROM HIS EXPEDITION EARLY JUST FOR YOUR BIRTHDAY, AND I WON'T HAVE YOU TREATING HIM LIKE THIS!
YOU CHANGE YOUR TUNE NOW, OR YOU'LL GO TO YOUR ROOM!
OH... IT'S MY BIRTHDAY, BUT AS SOON AS DAD WALKS IN, SUDDENLY HE'S SOOO IMPORTANT!
FINE!--
--I'LL GO TO MY ROOM!
HE'S BEEN SO FRESH LATELY...
IT'S ALL RIGHT, KATH-- HE'S JUST "PUNISHING" ME FOR BEING AWAY SO MUCH.

OASIS
"GO TO YOUR ROOM! GO TO YOUR ROOM!" --I WISH THEY'D ALL JUST GO AWAY AND LEAVE ME ALONE!
STUPID PRESENT! JUST LOOKS LIKE SOME KINDA STUPID FLASHLI--
--HUH?!
WHAT'S...
...WHAT'S IN THERE...?!
...IT LOOKS LIKE...
...GOTTA LET IT...
OASIS
KRAK
HOOOSSHHHH
HUHHHHH!

AND HE DROWNS IN THE DARK PURPLE ENERGY--
--IMMERSED IN THE THICK, LIQUID LIGHT, HE IS ASSAULTED WITH A RUSH OF ANCIENT IMAGES, SCENES FROM PREHISTORY--
--VISIONS OF A TIME THAT TIME HAS FORGOTTEN!
A MAD, MALEFIC SORCERER, CONJURING BEFORE AN EARTH-WELL, SUMMONS TO HIM A POWER ONLY ALLUDED TO IN CRUMBLING TOMES, ONLY WHISPERED OF IN THE DARKEST SHADOWS...
A POWER THAT FEEDS ON DREAMS AND ON WISHES, THE POWER TO RESHAPE THE WORLD --
--THE POWER OF A GOD!
BUT WHILE THE POWER IS NEAR-INFINITE...
...THE VESSEL IS STILL BUT A MAN!
HIS EVIL CAMPAIGN IS CHALLENGED BY ANOTHER SORCERER--

--HIS BROTHER!
THE MAD ONE'S TREACHERY AND HATRED BLINDS HIM AND LIMITS HIS IMAGINATION.
THIS ALLOWS HIS SIBLING TO PURGE THE MALEVOLENT ENERGIES FROM THE VILE MAGE--
--AND INTO A TINY CRYSTAL CHAMBER.
THERE IT IS IMPRISONED AND KEPT SECRETED FROM THE MEMORY OF MAN FOR ALL TIME!
...UNTIL NOW!
...POWER OF A GOD? ...CHANGE THE WORLD? ...COOL...
WELL, WE'LL JUST SEE WHAT THE WORLD WOULD BE LIKE IF I WAS IN CHARGE...
...YEAH, WE'LL JUST SEE...

DAWN, THE NEXT DAY, AT THE VENERABLE ESTATE OF JACK DRAKE--
NOK NOK
TIM...?

I'LL BE HAVIN' BREAKFAST ON THE TABLE IN A FEW MINUTES. D'YA WANT THREE EGGS'R FOUR?
NOK NOK
TIM...? ANSWER ME, LAD.

WELL, I'VE NEVER KNOWN A BOY THAT COULD SLEEP SO--
--?!
UP AN' GONE... ALREADY ?!

AND ALL ACROSS THE COUNTRY-- ACROSS THE WORLD--IT HAPPENS...
JORDYN? WHERE ARE YOU?

...AS SLEEPING AND UNBELIEVING PARENTS--
TYLER ...?

CASEY! YOU COME OUT HERE RIGHT NOW!
--COME TO THE SLOW AND TERRIFYING REALIZATION THAT--

GRETCHEN ...?!
HANK ?!
--THEY'RE GONE! THEY'RE GONE! ALL OF THE CHILDREN HAVE JUST ...DISAPPEARED!
JAKE!

MANCHESTER, ALABAMA--
HE'S GONE!
MAX, STOP! AT THAT SPEED, YOUR PACING REALLY WILL WEAR A HOLE IN THE CARPET!
AND I THOUGHT I WAS BEING LENIENT WHEN I GROUNDED HIM FOR JUST THE WEEKEND...! WHEN THAT BOY SHOWS UP, I'LL--
NOW, LET'S REMEMBER WHO IT IS WE'RE TALKING ABOUT HERE! BART IS--
SPECIAL REPORT
--MISSING! AUTHORITIES WISH TO REMIND US THAT PANICKING AND RIOTING WILL ONLY IMPEDE INVESTIGATIONS INTO THIS SITUATION! A STATE OF EMERGENCY HAS--
WHAT IS HE...? WHAT'S HE SAYING?!
--DECLARED AS GOVERNMENT AGENCIES LOOK INTO...
...THE STRANGE DISAPPEARANCE OF SEEMINGLY ALL JUVENILES BELOW THE AGE OF SEVENTEEN. ALL ARE URGED TO REMAIN CALM--
--AND REMAIN IN YOUR HOMES UNTIL FURTHER INFORMATION IS AVAILABLE. THE PRESIDENT IS EXPECTED...
...TO INTERRUPT PROGRAMMING WITH A STATEMENT WITHIN THE HOUR--
--IN HOPES OF QUELLING THE ALREADY-RAMPANT HYSTERIA THAT IS SWEEPING THE GLOBE! THE JUSTICE LEAGUE OF AMERICA IS BEING CONTACTED IN THEIR COMMAND CENTER ON--

--THE MOON--
--IN THE TECHNOLOGICAL MARVEL THAT IS THE WATCHTOWER, WHERE A HANDFUL OF THE EARTH'S GREATEST HEROES--
--(CURRENTLY, STEEL, FLASH, PLASTIC MAN, THE MARTIAN MANHUNTER, AND AQUAMAN)--
--HAVE BEEN WORKING DESPERATELY FOR THE PAST HALF-HOUR IN AN EFFORT TO DETERMINE THE CAUSE OF THIS WORLDWIDE CRISIS!
TO NO AVAIL...!
THIS IS SO FRUSTRATING-- I'VE NEVER FELT SO HELPLESS IN ALL MY LIFE!
TELL ME ABOUT IT.
I GET NOTHING, J'ONN!
NEITHER NORAD NOR S.T.A.R. LABS REPORT ANY ATMOSPHERIC OR SEISMIC ANOMALIES RECORDED IN THE LAST 24 HOURS! I'M REQUESTING A TERTIARY CHECK, BUT--
INCOMING!
GREEN LANTERN.
HEY, GUYS.

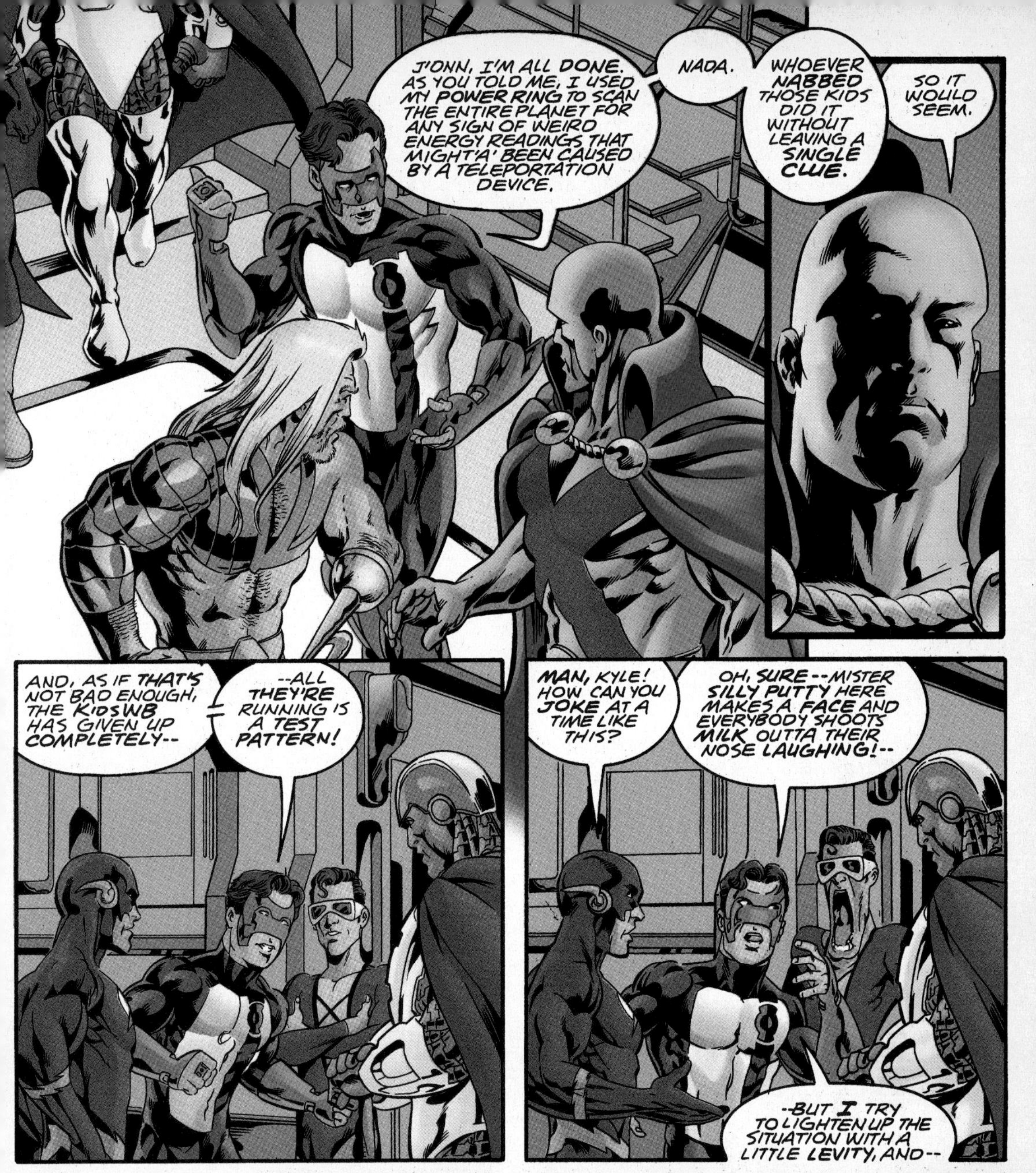

J'ONN, I'M ALL DONE. AS YOU TOLD ME, I USED MY POWER RING TO SCAN THE ENTIRE PLANET FOR ANY SIGN OF WEIRD ENERGY READINGS THAT MIGHT'A' BEEN CAUSED BY A TELEPORTATION DEVICE.
NADA.
WHOEVER NABBED THOSE KIDS DID IT WITHOUT LEAVING A SINGLE CLUE.
SO IT WOULD SEEM.
AND, AS IF THAT'S NOT BAD ENOUGH, THE KidsWB HAS GIVEN UP COMPLETELY--
--ALL THEY'RE RUNNING IS A TEST PATTERN!
MAN, KYLE! HOW CAN YOU JOKE AT A TIME LIKE THIS?
OH, SURE--MISTER SILLY PUTTY HERE MAKES A FACE AND EVERYBODY SHOOTS MILK OUTTA THEIR NOSE LAUGHING!--
--BUT I TRY TO LIGHTEN UP THE SITUATION WITH A LITTLE LEVITY, AND--

FINE, WALLY! AT LEAST STEEL HAS A SENSE OF--


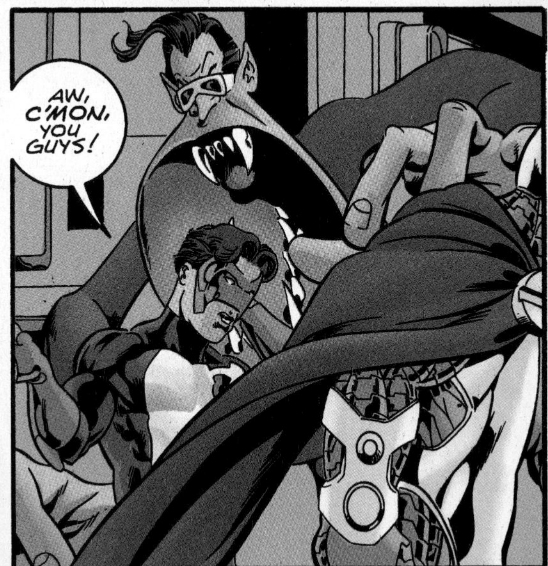

AW, C'MON, YOU GUYS!

KYLE'S RIGHT, J'ONN--WE HAVEN'T GOT A CLUE! WE HAVE STATE-OF-THE-ART DETECTION EQUIPMENT AND EVERY INFORMATION-GATHERING AGENCY IN THE WORLD AT OUR FINGERTIPS--
--AND WE'RE STILL COMING UP EMPTY!
IF THERE'S ONE THING I'VE LEARNED IN MY LIFE, BOTH HERE AND ON MARS, AQUAMAN, IT'S THAT EVERY MYSTERY LEAVES ITS CLUES--
--IT'S JUST A MATTER OF KNOWING WHERE TO LOOK...
WHAT CONCERNS ME MORE AT THE MOMENT, HOWEVER, IS THIS...
WE ARE SEEING THE EFFECTS THIS INCIDENT IS HAVING ON THE ADULT POPULATION OF THE WORLD: MASS HYSTERIA, PARANOIA, RIOTING, RELIGIOUS LEADERS AND ZEALOTS PROCLAIMING THE APOCALYPSE--
--BUT WHAT OF THE CHILDREN?
ABDUCTED FROM THEIR BEDS IN THE DEAD OF NIGHT...SPIRITED AWAY... WITHOUT THE PROTECTION AND SECURITY OF THEIR PARENTS...
TRULY THE STUFF OF NIGHTMARES...
WHEREVER THOSE CHILDREN MIGHT BE, ARTHUR...

"...THEY ARE UNDOUBTEDLY CONSUMED WITH TERROR!"
ELSEWHERE--
--IN A PLACE NOW KNOWN SIMPLY AS KIDWORLD--
--WHERE, BROUGHT ABOUT BY THE ABSENCE OF ANY PARENTAL FIGURES WHATSOEVER, THE ORDER OF THE DAY IS...
...PARTY!
ON AVERAGE, THE KIDS' REACTION TO THE MISSING ADULTS RUNS ABOUT 7.9 MINUTES OF FEAR AND/OR LOSS, FOLLOWED BY ROUGHLY 3.4 MINUTES OF MILD DISORIENTATION--
--AND THEN SUDDENLY... THE CLOUDS LIFT. THEIR EYES OPEN, SEEMINGLY FOR THE FIRST TIME EACH CHILD COMES TO THE REALIZATION THAT THE SHACKLES ARE OFF!
THAT THEY ARE LIBERATED FROM EVERY RULE OR RESPONSIBILITY EVER IMPOSED UPON THEM BY ANY AUTHORITY FIGURE!
THAT ANY ACTIVITY THEY WERE NOT TO DO OR WERE WARNED AGAINST BY GROWN-UPS--
TOYS
--IS NOW FAIR GAME!

-KAFF KAFF-
SOME, OF, COURSE, DISCOVER RATHER QUICKLY THAT SOME THINGS AREN'T AS MUCH FUN AS THEY HAD IMAGINED.
WHILE OTHERS--
C'MON, JUSTIN... JUMP!
I... I DUNNO. IT'S PRETTY HIGH... WHAT IF I FALL...?
AW, DON'T BE A WUSS! YOU'RE NOT GONNA FALL...YER GONNA FLY!
NOW JUMP!
FERGET IT, BRIAN! HE'S NOT GONNA DO IT...
...JUSTIN'S TOO MUCH OF A BABY TO BE A SUPER-HERO...!
I AM NOT A BABY!
JUMP! JUMP!

FWUMP
IT'S OKAY! I'VE GOT YOU!
AAHHHH!
HER NAME IS MARY MARVEL.
I HOPE THAT SCARED YOU ENOUGH TO KEEP YOU FROM DOING IT AGAIN!
NOW PROMISE ME THAT YOU WON'T JUMP OFF HOUSES WITH UMBRELLAS ANYMORE.
I PROMISE.
YEARS AGO SHE WAS GRANTED WONDROUS POWERS BY THE ENIGMATIC WIZARD SHAZAM WITH THE INTENTION THAT SHE USE THOSE POWERS TO FIGHT FOR JUSTICE AGAINST THE EVILS OF THE WORLD!
SHE, ALONG WITH HER BROTHER BILLY, IS ONE OF EARTH'S MIGHTIEST MORTALS!
TODAY, HOWEVER--
HEY! MAYBE IF WE GET BALLOONS!
YEAH, BALLOONS!
--SHE FEELS MORE LIKE EARTH'S MIGHTIEST BABY-SITTER!

AND SO IT GOES AROUND THE GLOBE--
--AS KIDWORLD'S ADOLESCENT HEROES OVERWHELMING PANDEMONIUM, WORKING CONTINUOUSLY TO DIVERT A PLANETFUL OF DISASTERS!
IN MANCHESTER, THE ARCHER ARROWETTE EXTINGUISHES A PAIR OF WOULD-BE ARSONISTS--

IN GATEWAY CITY, THE NEO-HERO WONDERGIRL HALTS A WAYWARD MINIVAN--

INFERNO DEFUSES SOME ENTERPRISING YOUNG PYROTECHNICIANS IN NEW MEXICO--

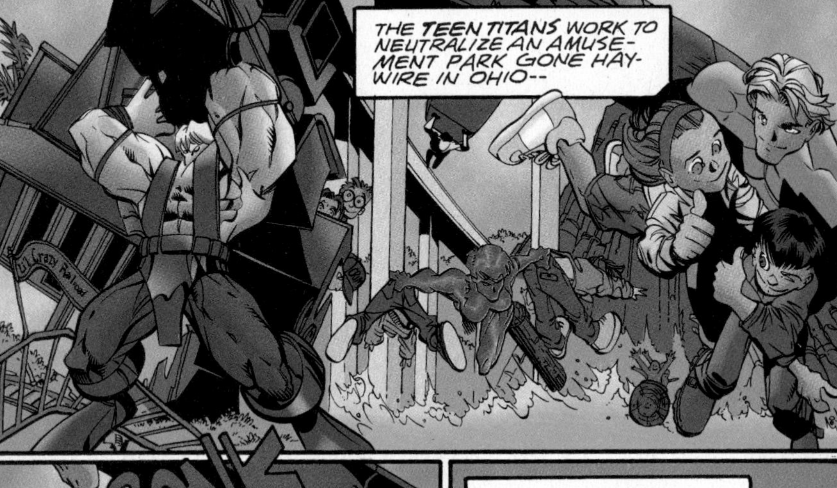
THE TEEN TITANS WORK TO NEUTRALIZE AN AMUSEMENT PARK GONE HAYWIRE IN OHIO--

BONK
OH, MAN! WE HIT CM3!
UNGH! STUPID ROLLER COASTER!

SPOILER RESCUES A WATERLOGGED SAILOR FROM HIS LESS-THAN-SEAWORTHY CRAFT IN GOTHAM HARBOR--

AND AT FERRIS AIRCRAFT, OSH KOSH, WISCONSIN --
THIS IS GONNA BE SO COOL...!
FERRIS AIRCRAFT RESTRICTED
EAGLE ONE TO TOWER-- REQUEST AUTHORIZATION FOR TAKE-OFF--
WOW! THIS IS JUST LIKE THE PLAYTENDO FLIGHT SIMULATOR ...ONLY LOUDER!
CONFIRMING YOUR CLEARANCE, TOWER--THIS IS MAJOR JONATHAN M. DENSON--
--ABOUT TO EMBARK ON THE MOST DANGEROUS MISSION EVER!
HEH HEH.
RUMBLE
SHOOM
HASTA LA VISTA, BABY!
ZOOM
CAN'T WAIT TO GET BACK TO CADMUS.
MAYBE THERE I CAN FIGURE OUT WHAT'S GOING ON --WHAT HAPPENED TO ALL THE ADULTS...
--AND WHAT TO DO WITH ALL THESE KI--
WHOA!
WHAT THE HECK IS THAT GUY DO--
WHAT AM I SAYING...?!

MEANWHILE, AT THE --
MONTGOMERY ZOO
...IF ALL THE ADULTS IN THE WORLD HAVE PULLED A HOUDINI, THEN THE GUY FLYING THAT JET...
...IS A KID !?!
'M'TELLING YA, DUDE --THIS IS GONNA BE SO FRESH!
MY UNCLE USETA WORK IN A PLACE LIKE THIS, AN' HE SHOWED ME HOW TO DO IT...

ALL YA GOTTA DO IS ACCESS THE RIGHT PROGRAMS... AN'...BAM!

"...WE'RE WATCHIN' THE DISCOVERY CHANNEL, DUDE!"
...TAWNY...?
RAAHHR!
ZWIPP
?
AND IN GOTHAM...
ARCADE
WELL, I'VE HAD 'BOUT ENOUGH O' YOU, JONAH HEX ...LET'S SEE WHO'S THE FASTEST DRAW NOW.
BLAM
BLAM
BLAM
NOW, THAT'S WHAT I CALL SHOOTIN'!
OW!
TWIP
HEY! WHO--

GO HOME.
STAY THERE. USE YOUR HEAD.
DON'T DO ANYTHING YOUR PARENTS WOULD TELL YOU NOT TO.
KATCH
THEN--
I FEEL LIKE I'M JUST WASTING MY TIME--DEALING WITH THE RESULTS OF THE PROBLEM INSTEAD OF THE PROBLEM ITSELF!
I'VE GOTTA FIGURE OUT WHAT HAPPENED--AND THEN, MORE IMPORTANT, HOW TO FIX IT!
MEANWHILE--
THERE'S OUR PINT-SIZED CHUCK YEAGER NOW! MAN, HE MUST HAVE THIS THING GOING CLOSE TO MACH 3!
BUT I'LL BET HIS HEART IS RACING FASTER! POOR KID'S TERRI-FIED!
S'CUSE ME THERE, SPORT, BUT I'M GONNA HAVE TO ASK YOU TO PULL OVER...
...WOULDJA MIND CUTTING THE ENGINES, PLEASE ...?
THANKS.

OKAY, I'VE GOT THE KID'S CONFIDENCE. LET'S HOPE I DON'T SCREW THIS UP!
THE THING'S MOVING SO FAST THAT IF I TRY TO STOP IT ALL AT ONCE, IT'LL JUST COME APART IN MY HANDS!
HAFTA BE DELICATE WITH MY TACTILE TELEKINESIS...
...FIND THE RIGHT LEVERAGE TO SLOW THIS BIRD DOWN GRADUALLY...
UNGH!
C'MON, BABY ...WE CAN DO THIS...!

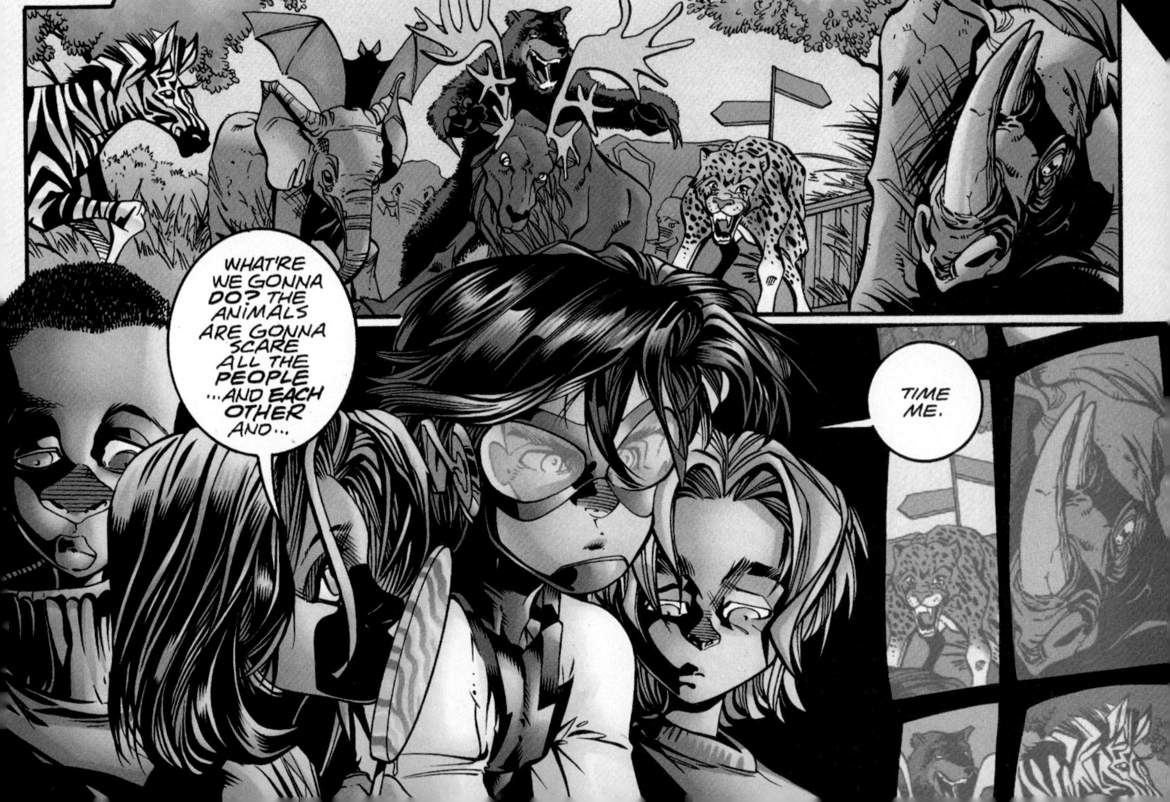
WHILE--
WHAT'RE WE GONNA DO? THE ANIMALS ARE GONNA SCARE ALL THE PEOPLE ...AND EACH OTHER AND...
TIME ME.

sec. 00:02
MAMMALS
MARSUPIALS
BIRDS
sec. 00:14
sec. 00:27
sec. 00:30
HABITAT
LOCKING
SEQUENCE:
RESET!
taka
taka
tak
sec. 00:35
sec. 00:32
WE'RESORRY
WEWON'T
DOITAGAIN
WEPROMISE!
GOOD.

WELL, THAT'S A FINE JOB, IF I DO SAY SO MYSELF. I BROUGHT THIS BABY DOWN WITH-OUT HER SHAKING APART...
...BUT THAT MIGHT NOT BE SO TRUE OF OUR PILOT!
C'MON OUT, "MAVERICK"-- THIS RIDE'S OVER!
Y'KNOW, I DON'T WANNA TELL YOU WHAT TO DO OR ANYTHING, BUT HOW ABOUT A SUGGESTION...
NO MORE PLANES.
no more planes... no more planes...
I THINK I NEED TO LIE DOWN FOR A LITTLE BIT...
YOU DO THAT.
WHUMPP
HEY, SUPERBOY, IS THAT KID GONNA BE ALL RIGHT?
HUH? OH, HI, IMPULSE. YEAH, HE'LL BE FINE... ONCE THE WORLD STOPS SPINNING.
OH.
IS THAT GONNA HAPPEN, TOO?
AH, FERGET IT.

WELL, SOMETHING'S HAPPENED! WHERE ARE ALL THE--
THAT'S WHAT WE'VE GOT TO FIND OUT.

HEY, ROBIN. HOW'D YOU FIND US?
RADAR. ASIDE FROM YOUR FRIEND IN THE JET--

--YOU TWO ARE THE ONLY THINGS SHOWING UP ON IT.
I FIGURE BETWEEN THE THREE OF US, WE MIGHT PUT TOGETHER WHAT HAPPENED.

WHY US?
COOL BIKE.
WHAT ABOUT THE JLA?
THEY ON STRIKE'R SOME-THIN'?

DON'T BE A DOPE, BART.
IF ALL THE ADULTS ARE GONE, THEN SO IS THE JLA.
THERE IS NO JUSTICE LEAGUE.

NO. IF THEY'RE GONE, THEN WE'RE ALL THERE IS.
WE'RE IT!

SO...
WOW.
WHATTA WE DO?!

SHORTLY--
NOTHING BUT "SNOW." THE COMPUTER'S SET TO CONTINUE SCANNING FOR ANY BROADCAST SIGNAL...
...BUT I WOULDN'T COUNT ON IT.
ALL COMMUNICATIONS SYSTEMS--EVERYTHING!--ARE SHUT DOWN! THERE'RE NO ADULTS TO KEEP THINGS RUNNING! UNLESS WE DO SOMETHING FAST--
--SOON WE'LL BE OUT OF FOOD, WATER, ELECTRICITY.
I'LL TRY TO ESTABLISH CONTACT WITH THE JUSTICE LEAGUE'S WATCHTOWER.
EVEN IF THEY'RE NOT THERE...
...MAYBE THEIR COMPUTER CAN GIVE US A CLUE WHY--
HEY, ROBIN!

HOWCUM YOU KEEP YOUR OLD COSTUME IN A GLASS CASE LIKE THIS?
DOES IT SMELL FUNNY'R, SOMETHIN' ...?
GET AWAY FROM THERE!
ZWIP
THERE'S NO RESPONSE FROM THE WATCHTOWER AT ALL.
BECAUSE NOBODY'S THERE?
NO. BECAUSE IT'S NOT THERE.
ACCORDING TO THE COMPUTER...
...THERE IS NO WATCH-TOWER!

-KRKL-KRK-KK-AWCETT CITY, WHERE-KRRRKK-PANDEMONIUM IN THE STREETS-KRKL-
HEY! WE'RE GETTING SOMETHING.
-KRRKKK-10-YEAR-OLD BOY-
-KRRK-SLAMMED A TRACTOR TRAILER INTO A NEIGHBORING-KRKKL-KRKKK-
-KRKKL-WRECKING BALL THROUGH-KRKKKK-
-ILLY BATSON FOR-KRKKL-
--KK-STATION WHIZ, FAWC-KKKK-ITY. I'M ALL ALONE HERE, AND WONDERING IF-KKRK-NY-BODY'S LISTENING... IF THERE'S ANY HOPE. -KKKL-
...AND WHERE IS THE JUSTICE LEAGUE?
WOW. DOES HE MEAN US?
HE DOES NOW.
...BATSON...?

THE WATCHTOWER--
--CHECK OUT A FEW HUNCHES ON MY OWN. I'LL GET BACK TO YOU LATER.
--DOING EVERYTHING WE CAN, MISTER PRESIDENT. WHOEVER IS RESPONSIBLE FOR THIS HAS COVERED THEIR TRACKS WELL! I'M SORRY I CAN'T GIVE YOU A MORE OPTIMISTIC REPORT, BUT...
UNFORTUNATELY, SUPERMAN, I HAVE NOTHING TO OFFER BUT HOPE. AN OCCURRENCE OF THIS NATURE IS ENTIRELY OUT OF MY REALM OF EXPERTISE--
THE U.N. HAS NO PROTOCOLS OR ACTIONS TO TAKE, SHOULD HALF THE POPULATION SIMPLY VANISH FROM THE FACE OF THE EARTH! PLEASE KEEP ME POSTED ON ANY PROGRESS YOU MIGHT MAKE.
I'M CONFIDENT THAT WE'LL FIND SOMETHING, SIR...
...WE HAVE TO.
J'ONN, HOW CAN WE BE MISSING THIS? THERE MUST BE SOME TRACE EVIDENCE --SOMETHING THAT WE CAN GO ON TO UNRAVEL THIS THING!
I MEAN, IT SEEMS TO ME THAT WE'VE COVERED EVERYTHING THREE TIMES OVER! DIDN'T YOU SAY THAT SOLVING A MYSTERY IS KNOWING WHERE TO LOOK?
WELL, THEN... MAYBE THE REAL QUESTION IS...

--WHERE AREN'T WE LOOKING!?
THE BAT-CAVE.
--PULATION SIMPLY VANISH FROM THE FACE OF THE EARTH--SKK-- VANISH FROM THE FACE OF THE EARTH--SKK-- FROM THE--SKK-- VANISH FROM THE FACE OF THE--
--FACE OF THE EARTH!--SKK-- FACE OF THE EARTH!--SKK-- THE EARTH! --SKK--THE--
VIDEO CAPTURE
LINK
BEGIN SEQUENCE.
SSKITTTCH

SOMEWHERE... DARK...
HE CALLS HIMSELF BEDLAM--
--(HE CALLS HIS NEW WORLD THAT, AS WELL...)--
--AND THE AIR CRACKLES AND BENDS WITH VIOLENT VIOLET MAGIK AS HE EXERCISES HIS NEWFOUND, NEAR INFINITE POWERS, HIS EVERY WHIM AND DESIRE INSTANTLY REALIZED BEFORE HIS DARKLY GLOWING EYES!
THE IMAGINATION OF A THIRTEEN-YEAR-OLD KID BROUGHT TO LIFE (ALBEIT WITH A ROILING BRUISE COLORED TINGE)--
WITH HIS GIANT, NAMELESS BENEFACTOR STANDING NEARBY IN SILENT ATTENDANCE, THE BOY WHO WAS ONCE MATTHEW STUART BOGGLES AT THE POSSIBILITIES OF THIS POWER HE NOW WIELDS--
--AND UTTERS HIS FIRST WORDS...
...AS A GOD!
THIS IS... SWEET!!!
WITH THESE POWERS, I CAN DO ANYTHING, HAVE ANYTHING, BE ANYTHING THAT I WANT! I CAN CREATE ANYTHING JUST BY THINKING ABOUT IT!
I THOUGHT UP A WHOLE WORLD, AND ALL IT TOOK WAS USING THE RIGHT... VESSEL? --USING THE MOST POWERFUL CHILD'S MIND AS A... A CONDUIT... TO KEEP THAT WORLD EXISTING!
AND THE MORE THAT THEY BELIEVE --THE ADULTS AND THE CHILDREN, TOO --THE MORE IMAGINATION THEY FEED ME WITH--
BEDLAM
BEDLAM
PLAYPEN
TABOO
KILLER MAC

--THE MORE POWERFUL I BECOME!
baseball player!
SOON I'LL BE INVINCIBLE! UNSTOPPABLE! THEN THEY'LL SEE...
race car driver!
YEAH, THEN MOM AND DAD WILL...
...THEN...
...MOM AND...
...DAD...?
WHAT... WAIT, WHAT'S...

THE MUTE CREATURE'S EYES FLASH BRIEFLY IN SILENT DISAPPROVAL--
--AN ALMOST IMPERCEPTIBLE NOD--
--AS KNIVES OF ENERGY STAB OUT TO..."CORRECT" ...THE SITUATION!
HURHHH!
...YES, THEN THEY'LL SEE!
THEN THEY'LL ALL SEE!

MEANWHILE, IN THE ADULT-FREE, KID-INFESTED FAWCETT CITY--
OKAY-- THERE IT IS.
THE RADIO AND TV STATION WE SAW?! WHADDA WE GONNA DO HERE?
WHIZ
WE'RE NOT GONNA DO ANYTHING... I JUST WANT TO HAVE A WORD WITH...
...HIM!
SUPERBOY?! ROBIN?! KID FLASH?!
I GET THAT A LOT.
WH-WHAT ARE YOU GUYS DOING ...H-HERE...?
SUPERBOY... IMPULSE, EXCUSE BILLY AND ME FOR A SECOND.

ACTUALLY, I WAS HOPING THAT THERE WAS SOMETHING YOU COULD DO...OR MORE SPECIFICALLY, SOMETHING YOU COULD SAY...?
I KNOW WHO YOU ARE...
WE COULD REALLY USE YOUR HELP.
I MEAN, THERE'S N-NOTHING THAT I CAN DO.
ON AIR
BUT IT'S NOT THAT SIMPLE. I'M--I'M AFRAID!
ALL OF THE ADULTS ARE MISSING. WHAT IF I SAY THE MAGIC WORD AND TURN INTO CAPTAIN MARVEL ...WHAT'LL HAPPEN?
WHAT IF I BECOME A GROWN-UP AND...

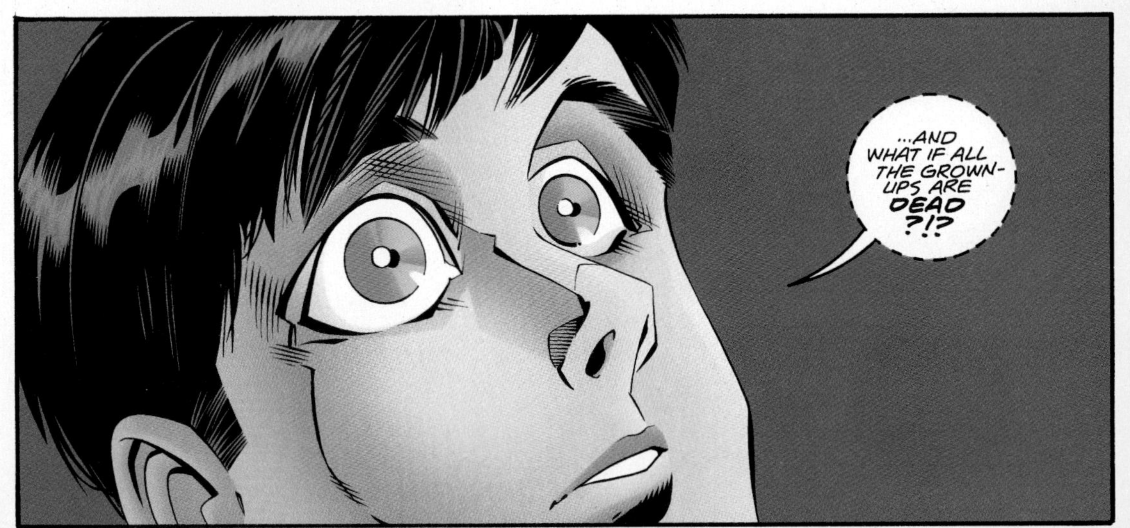
...AND WHAT IF ALL THE GROWN-UPS ARE DEAD ?!?

I DON'T THINK THAT
WHADDAYA THINK THEY'RE TALKING ABOUT...?

HMMM? OH, PROBABLY...
...YOU!

OH.

HEY, WAITAMINNIT. WHADDAYA MEAN, ME--?!
WHY WOULD THEY BE TALKING ABOUT ME?

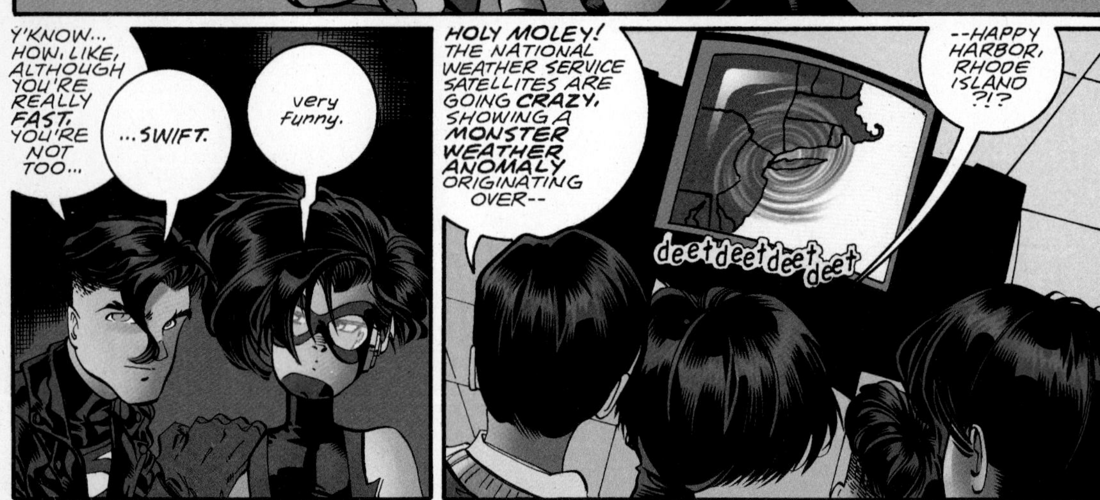
Y'KNOW... HOW, LIKE, ALTHOUGH YOU'RE REALLY FAST, YOU'RE NOT TOO...
...SWIFT.
very funny.
HOLY MOLEY! THE NATIONAL WEATHER SERVICE SATELLITES ARE GOING CRAZY, SHOWING A MONSTER WEATHER ANOMALY ORIGINATING OVER--
--HAPPY HARBOR, RHODE ISLAND ?!?
deet deet deet deet deet

THE WATCHTOWER...
--CARBON DATING VARIOUS SAMPLES-- OF EVERYTHING-- FROM ALL AROUND THE BATCAVE, ONLY TO DISCOVER THAT IT WAS ALL THE SAME AGE! ROUGHLY SEVENTEEN HOURS OLD!
EVERYTHING-- DOWN TO THE MINUTEST DETAIL-- EVERY-THING ABOUT THIS..."EARTH" IS A SIMULA-TION, A REPLICA DESIGNED TO MAINTAIN THE ILLUSION THAT IT'S BUSINESS AS USUAL.
...BUT THE TRUTH IS, THE KIDS WEREN'T ABDUCTED...
...WE WERE!
WHAT ?!?
THAT'S IMPOSSIBLE!
WHO COULD'VE ...WHO HAS THAT KINDA POWER ...?
THE CHILDREN!? WHAT ARE THEY UP AGAINST !?!
THEN WE CAN ONLY HOPE THE YOUNGER HEROES WILL BE WORKING...
...TO GET THE SITUATION UNDER CONTROL.
HEY, THAT'S RIGHT! I FORGOT THAT THE TITANS'LL BE THERE TO RESTORE SOME ORDER...
AND THEY'VE GOT ROBIN...
SUPERBOY IS THERE... AND THE NEW WONDER GIRL!
OH, NO!
NONO NONONO NONO NO!
WALLY? WHAT IS IT?
BART...!--
--THEY'VE GOT BART!

MEANWHILE, BACK ON KID-WORLD, AT THE WHIZ STUDIOS...
HAPPY HARBOR!?! ISN'T THAT WHERE THE OLD--
--JLA HEADQUARTERS IS, AND WHERE THE LEGION--
ZWIP

--WAS HANGING OUT FOR A WHILE...?
YUP THAT'S IT.
ZWIP
YOU GUYS'VE GOTTA SEE THIS!

BILLY, ARE YOU SURE THERE'S NOTHING YOU CAN DO? I MEAN, C'MON, YOU'RE A HERO AND--

NO. DON'T YOU SEE...?

IT WON'T DO ANYONE ANY GOOD IF I DISAPPEAR, TOO...
...I'M JUST A KID...BUT MAYBE I CAN THINK OF SOME-THING ELSE...

WHAT WAS THAT ALL ABOUT?
NOTHING. IT'S OKAY. I THOUGHT THAT MAYBE BILLY COULD HELP US...
...BUT I GUESS I WAS WRONG.
EXIT

AND SHORTLY, ON A CLIFFSIDE OVER-LOOKING THE AFOREMENTIONED HAPPY HARBOR...
WOW! WEIRD WEATHER WHATSIS WAS AN UNDER-STATEMENT!
LOOK AT THIS PLACE!
IT'S LIKE SOME KIND OF TWISTED NIGHTMARE BROUGHT TO LIFE! WHAT COULD POSSIBLY BE--
RMMBL
WHOA!
UH OH!
MOVE! THE GROUND'S GIVING WAY!

SUPERBOY, CAN YOU PULL US UP...?
I DON'T LIKE THE LOOKS OF THIS!
OH! THIS IS GOOD!

WHIZ--
AWW, MAN! I MUST LOOK LIKE A CHICKEN!
ROBIN PROBABLY THINKS I'M LETTING MY FEAR OF THE UNKNOWN KEEP ME FROM BECOMING CAPTAIN MARVEL!
WHEN I JUST MIGHT BE OUR ONLY HOPE!
THE OLD WIZARD GAVE ME THE POWER TO BE CAPTAIN MARVEL SO THAT I COULD HELP PEOPLE--DO WHAT'S RIGHT! IT'S MY DUTY...
...MY RESPONSI-BILITY.
and we could use some help right now...
ROBIN'S RIGHT... I CAN'T JUST SIT HERE, HOPING FOR A BETTER IDEA... I'VE GOT TO TRY! C'MON, BILLY-- YOU CAN DO IT--
--EVEN IF YOU ARE A LITTLE SCARED--
--JUST SAY THE MAGIC WORD...
...SAY SHAZAM! SAY--
SHA-

-ZAM!

HIS NAME IS BILLY BATSON.

YEARS AGO, UPON MEETING AN **ANCIENT WIZARD** IN A CAVE, HE WAS GRANTED THE ABILITY TO TRANSFORM HIMSELF INTO THE **MIGHTIEST MORTAL** ON **EARTH**--

--TO FIGHT FOR **JUSTICE AND GOODNESS** AS THE INVINCIBLE Captain MARVEL!

ALL THE YOUNG BOY NEED DO TO **TRIGGER** THE **MAGICAL TRANSFORMATION** WAS TO **UTTER** THE OLD MAN'S **NAME**--

--SHAZAM!

THAT **USUALLY** DID THE TRICK...

TODAY, HOWEVER...

...THAT AIN'T HAPPENIN'!
WHAT TH--?!
I'M STILL ME! PLAIN OLD BILLY BATSON!
AFTER WAKING UP THIS MORNING TO FIND THAT ALL THE GROWN-UPS HAD MYSTERIOUSLY DIS-APPEARED LAST NIGHT, I WAS KINDA NERVOUS ABOUT CHANGING INTO THE BIG RED CHEESE --
-- IF I TURNED INTO MY GROWN-UP SELF, WHERE WOULD I GO--?
--BUT NOTHING HAPPENED! THE LIGHTNING STRUCK, BUT I DIDN'T CHANGE!?! I DIDN'T GO--
?!?
WAIT A MINUTE! WHERE THE HECK AM I?!
THE MAGIC WORD DIDN'T CAUSE THE CHANGE, BUT SOMEHOW I GOT BOOSTED HERE?!?...SOME KINDA...LIMBO ...IN BETWEEN SPACE...
THERE'S EARTH RIGHT DOWN THERE, SO I CAN...
ER...HANG ON... IF THAT'S EARTH DOWN THERE, THEN WHAT'S...

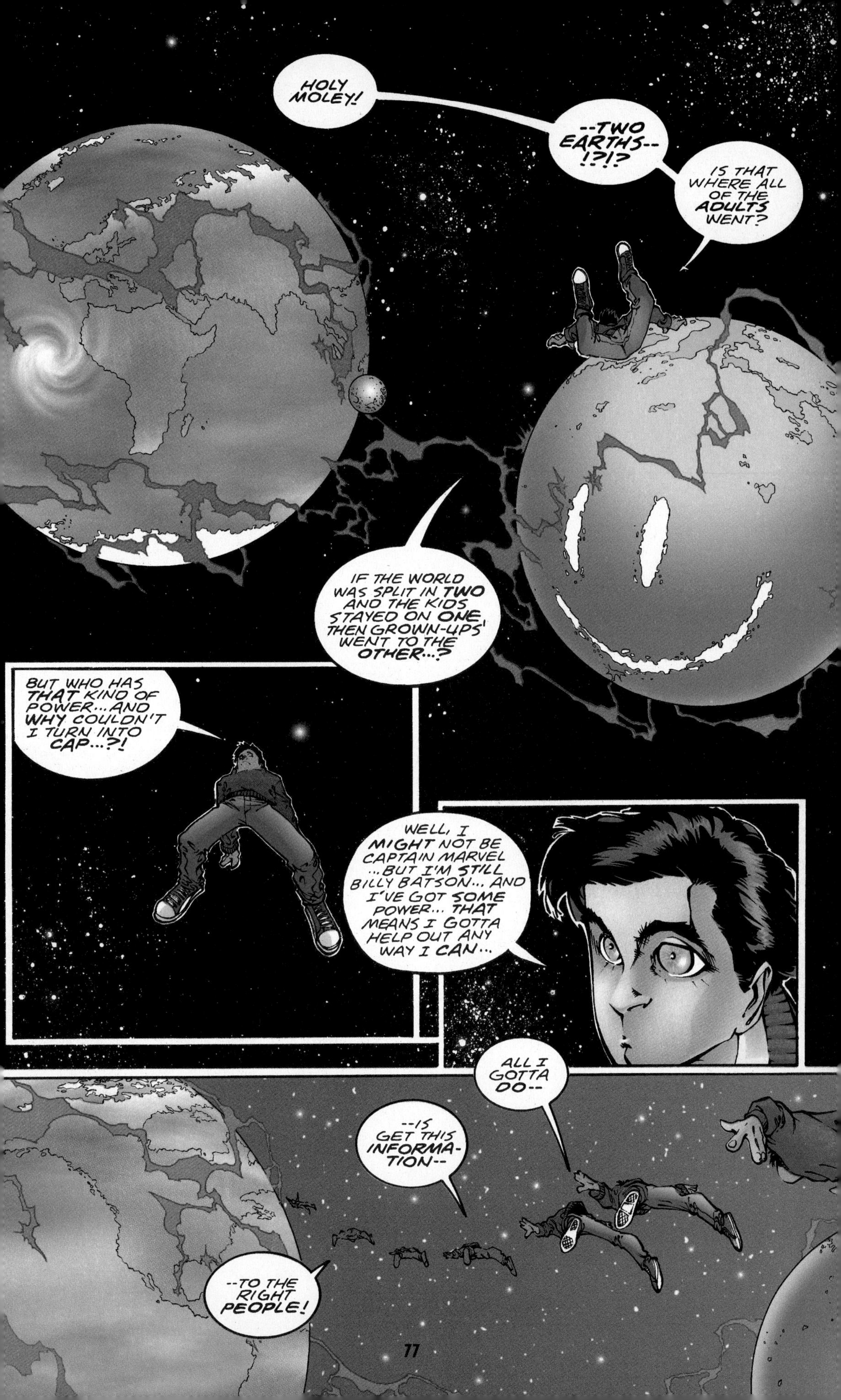
HOLY MOLEY!
--TWO EARTHS-- !?!?
IS THAT WHERE ALL OF THE ADULTS WENT?
IF THE WORLD WAS SPLIT IN TWO AND THE KIDS STAYED ON ONE, THEN GROWN-UPS WENT TO THE OTHER...?
BUT WHO HAS THAT KIND OF POWER... AND WHY COULDN'T I TURN INTO CAP...?!
WELL, I MIGHT NOT BE CAPTAIN MARVEL ...BUT I'M STILL BILLY BATSON... AND I'VE GOT SOME POWER... THAT MEANS I GOTTA HELP OUT ANY WAY I CAN...
ALL I GOTTA DO--
--IS GET THIS INFORMATION--
--TO THE RIGHT PEOPLE!

MEANWHILE, ON THE KIDWORLD--
HEY!--
--WHERE SUPERBOY, IMPULSE, AND ROBIN ARE RECEIVING A LESS-THAN-WARM WELCOME FROM THE SCENERY (!) AS THEY UNKNOWINGLY CLOSE IN ON THE ONE RESPONSIBLE FOR THE RECENT... BEDLAM!
IT'S LIKE THE TREES AND ROCKS SUDDENLY CAME TO LIFE AND DECIDED TO GET MAD AT US ALL AT THE SAME TIME!
SKRRICH
SKRATT
SSKRR RRICH
IMPULSE! CAN YOU DO ANYTHING...?!
NOT WHILE I'M HANGING ON TO HIM AND YOU'RE HANGING ON TO ME!
I NEED SOME TRACTION!
WELL, SOMEBODY DO SOMETHING!
SKRTCCCH
SKRATTLE
SKRRRT
THESE BRANCHES ARE-- OUCH!

I'M TRYING, SUPERBOY--I CAN'T GET A LINE OUT! I NEED A CLEAR SHOT AND THE TREES ARE BLOCKING--
HEY, D'YOU GUYS NOTICE... THIS IS JUST LIKE "NAZI DINOSAURS FROM VENUS!"
IT'S-- WHAT?
AAHHH! WILL YOU GUYS STOP YAKKIN' AND DO SOME-THING?!
SKRRRT
SKRTIT
SKRCCH
Y'KNOW... THE VIDEO GAME! "NAZI DINOSAURS FROM VENUS"...!
IT'S GOT TREES LIKE THIS, AND HIDDEN PITS AND ACID SNOW AND THESE HUGE NAZI--
HRR RRAA AAAH R
--DINO-SAURS!

THERE'S THE OPENING I WAS LOOKING FOR...
HANG ON, BOYS!--
WHHIPP
--IT'S ABOUT TO GET REAL JERKY!
!
THWING
THP
THP
THP
RAHHHHH
WHOA!
WHOA!
WHOA!
SNAP

TUMBLE
THUMP
BART! WHIP UP A WHIRLWIND-- GET THAT THING IN THE AIR!
BUMP
YOU GOT IT!
RRRR?
ZWIPP
VZZ
VZZ
VZZZ
EASY, BARNEY!
SUPERBOY-- HE'S YOURS!
OH, I DON'T WANT HIM! LET'S JUST SEND HIM BACK TO URANUS--
BOW
--I MEAN... VENUS...!
REEEEEE!

...URANUS?
THERE'S YOUR "TEAMWORK," WONDER BOY-- WHAT'D YA THINK OF THAT?!
GREAT. MAYBE NEXT TIME WE CAN DO IT ON PURPOSE...
WELL, PARDON ME, MISTER PERFECT. FORGIVE US FOR DOING SOMETHING RIGHT! WHAT'RE YOU--
WOW. LOOK...
YOU ARE NOW ENTERIN
BEDLAM
LEASE WATCH STEP
YOU MUST BE THIS TALL TO ENTER BEDLAM
ONE W
STOP
ENTRA
THIS WAY
NOT THIS WAY
THAT WASN'T LIKE THAT BEFORE...
I HAVE A FUNNY FEELING WE'RE ABOUT TO FIND OUT JUST HOW GOOD A TEAM WE ARE...!
FUNNY LIKE SOUTH PARK IS FUNNY, OR FUNNY-- AH FORGET IT!

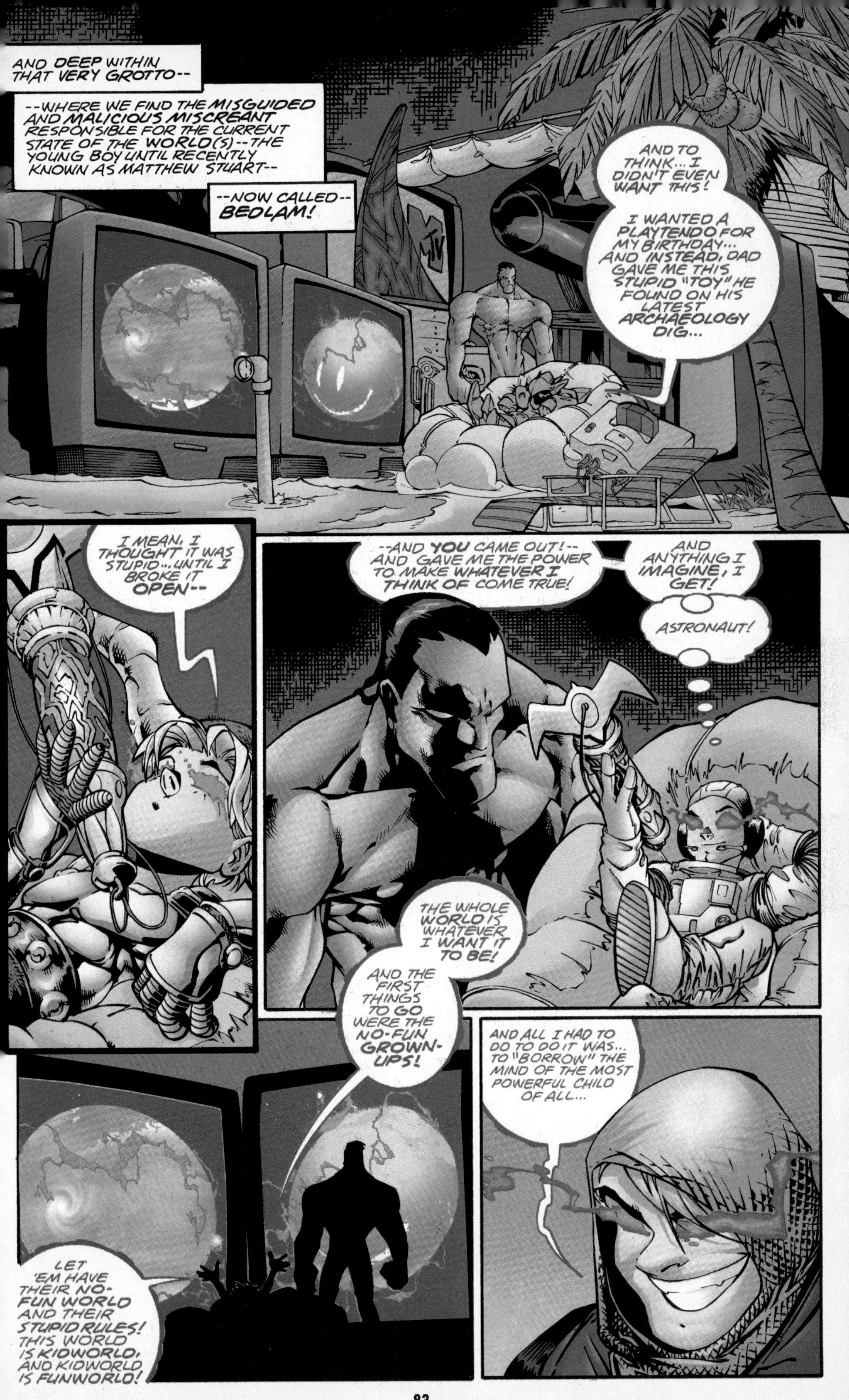
AND DEEP WITHIN THAT VERY GROTTO--
--WHERE WE FIND THE MISGUIDED AND MALICIOUS MISCREANT RESPONSIBLE FOR THE CURRENT STATE OF THE WORLD(S)--THE YOUNG BOY UNTIL RECENTLY KNOWN AS MATTHEW STUART--
--NOW CALLED-- BEDLAM!
AND TO THINK... I DIDN'T EVEN WANT THIS!
I WANTED A PLAYTENDO FOR MY BIRTHDAY... AND INSTEAD, DAD GAVE ME THIS STUPID "TOY" HE FOUND ON HIS LATEST ARCHAEOLOGY DIG...
I MEAN, I THOUGHT IT WAS STUPID... UNTIL I BROKE IT OPEN--
--AND YOU CAME OUT!-- AND GAVE ME THE POWER TO MAKE WHATEVER I THINK OF COME TRUE!
AND ANYTHING I IMAGINE, I GET!
ASTRONAUT!
THE WHOLE WORLD IS WHATEVER I WANT IT TO BE!
AND THE FIRST THINGS TO GO WERE THE NO-FUN GROWN-UPS!
LET 'EM HAVE THEIR NO-FUN WORLD AND THEIR STUPID RULES! THIS WORLD IS KIDWORLD, AND KIDWORLD IS FUNWORLD!
AND ALL I HAD TO DO TO DO IT WAS... TO "BORROW" THE MIND OF THE MOST POWERFUL CHILD OF ALL...

AND THE LONGER IT STAYS THIS WAY-- THE MORE THAT PEOPLE BELIEVE IN WHAT I'VE DONE--THE MORE POWERFUL I BECOME...UNTIL SOON I'LL TRULY HAVE THE POWER--
--OF A GOD!
BUT FIRST, I GUESS, I'LL HAFTA TAKE CARE OF THESE "SUPER-DOPES" THAT ARE ABOUT TO GET CHOMPED UP BY MY "WATCHDOG"...
...MY LITTLE NAZI DINOSAUR FROM--
HEY! I COULD...
NAZI DINOSAURS FROM VENUS

NO! I HAVE NO TIME FOR VIDEO GAMES! I--

I HAVE ENTIRE WORLDS AT MY FINGERTIPS. I--

I...I WANT...

...I WANNA PLAY! THIS WAS S'POSED TO BE...
...FUN...!

GENERALLY MOTIONLESS IN ITS MUTE ATTENDANCE, BEDLAM'S SILENT BENEFACTOR STIRS BRIEFLY, NOTING ITS... "AVATAR'S" SUDDEN LUCIDITY--

--RETURNING, THEN, TO ITS IMPASSIVE STANCE AS MAGICKAL ENERGIES DASH OUT FROM ITS EYES, ENVELOPING THE YOUNG BOY--

--RE-ESTABLISHING ...THE POWER!
YESSS.
OF COURSE.
YOU'RE RIGHT--
--PLENTY OF TIME FOR PLAY, ONCE THESE THREE...
...ANNOYANCES...
...ARE DEALT WITH...!

ADULTWORLD--
--OR RATHER, ABOUT 240,000 MILES ABOVE IT, IN THE WATCHTOWER--THE LUNAR HEADQUARTERS OF THE JUSTICE LEAGUE OF AMERICA.
...CONFIRMING BATMAN'S FINDINGS THAT, WHILE WE FIRST BELIEVED THAT IT WAS THE CHILDREN WHO WERE ABDUCTED IN THE NIGHT, THE ACTUAL TRUTH IS THAT... WE WERE!?!
THE EARTH THAT'S SPINNING BELOW US, AND EVERYTHING ON IT, IS AN EXACT DUPLICATE OF THE EARTH WE KNOW! WE CAN ONLY ASSUME THAT THE KIDS ARE STILL ON THE ORIGINAL!
WHOEVER'S RESPONSIBLE FOR THIS IS WIELDING CONSIDERABLE POWER ON A LEVEL BEYOND COMPREHENSION. WITH NO CONTACT MADE, NO DEMANDS ISSUED, WE CAN ONLY GUESS AT A MOTIVE...
I HAVE THE ORACLE CHECKING SEVERAL POSSIBLE SUSPECTS, BUT IT'S MORE LIKELY THAT THIS IS SOMEONE WE'VE NEVER CONFRONTED BEFORE. THAT'S THE DAUNTING ASPECT...
"--BETTER THE DEVIL WE KNOW..."
I'LL BE IN TOUCH.

ANOTHER SOME-WHERE ELSE...
I CAN SMELL YOU, RUNT.
DO YOU MIND IF I CALL YOU... CLARICCCCCE?
AND THIS IS SUPPOSED TO SCARE ME HOW?
OH, NOT YOU. ME. AT LEAST, I THINK IT'S ME ...THEY TELL ME THIS IS ALL IN MY MIND, Y'KNOW, OR YOURS!
HAVE A SEAT! STAY FOR DINNER! YOU'LL HAVE TO TAKE OFF YOUR SHOES, THOUGH.
WE'RE HAVING CHINESE. LAST NIGHT WE HAD HUNGARIAN AND WE HAD TO TAKE OFF OUR--
I'LL STAND.
OH, SO LIKE THE BAT, AREN'T WE...?
KINDA TOUGH LIVING UP TO THAT STANDARD, THOUGH, ISN'T IT? I MEAN, C'MON! HE'S BATMAN!
MAKES YA FEEL KINDA... INADEQUATE, DOESN'T IT? INSIGNIFICANT...?...
...SMALL...?
...YEAH ...BUT...

AND THOSE TWO BOZOS YOU'VE HOOKED UP WITH...? WITH THEIR SPIFFY SUPER-POWERS...?! THEY'RE LIKE GODS!
WHAT COULD YOU POSSIBLY BRING TO THAT TEAM?! SOME BAT-TOYS? THAT LONG STICK-THING YOU CARRY?...
NO!
NOTHING!
NADA!
YOU'RE JUST BAGGAGE TO THEM!
YOU'RE OUTTA YOUR MIND IF YOU THINK--
THAT'S IT, THEN...?
HUH?
THAT'S ALL I HAVE TO DO, ISN'T IT? I MEAN, I'M MAKING THIS--
--THERE'S SOMEBODY ELSE WHO'S MAKING IT REAL, BUT IT'S MY THOUGHTS THAT KINDA WROTE THE RULES...
SO ALL I HAVE TO DO IS TO THINK OF DOING...
...SOMETHING LIKE THIS...
OOOO OOOT!
SHOOP
UFF!
HAHA HAHA!
QUICK, SUPERBOY! TAG ME!
SHOOP
HUH? ROBIN?
JUST DO IT!

fwink
ROBIN?!?
YEAH, AND YOU KNOW SOMETHING, TIN-MAN...?
...TO ME, KRYPTONITE IS JUST ANOTHER ROCK!
KTRANNG
K-K-K-K-K-K-K-K-
AND NOW, I BELIEVE, IF I THINK ABOUT IT HARD ENOUGH...
fwink
THAT'S GOOD TO KNOW.
AND NOW, LITTLE INSECT, PREPARE TO MEET YOUR DOOM AT THE HANDS OF--
BART, QUICK! TAG ME!
HUH? OKAY...

twink
YOU WERE SAYING...?
OOK!
GRUFFF!
POW
twink
I TOOK CARE OF LI'L METALLO.
I POPPED LI'L... BIG GRODD...
OH, NO! THAT MEANS BART IS--
--MATCHING WITS WITH THE LI'L JOKER!

NO! NOOO! MAKE HIM STOP! I CAN'T TAKE ANYMORE! I CAN'T! I WON'T!
WHY? WHY? WHY? WHY? WHY? WHY? WHY? WHY? WHY? WHY? WHY? WHY? WHY? WHY? WHY? WHY? WHY? WHY? WHY? WHY? WHY? WHY? WHY? WHY? WHY? WHY? WHY? WHY? WHY? WHY?
NO! YOU WIN! YOU WIN! DRIVING ME--
twink
BART ...?
HUH ?
SHOOP
...LET'S GO!

OKAY, THAT WAS INTERESTING! NOW WHY DON'T WE FIND OUT WHO THIS BEDLAM CREEP IS...!

ADULTWORLD--
HAPPY HARBOR--
IT WOULD APPEAR, BILLY, THAT YOU'VE LED US DIRECTLY TO THE ROOT OF THIS PROBLEM...
I AGREE, J'ONN, BUT TELL ME...
...WHAT DO YOU MAKE OF THAT?!
HEY! WHAT'RE YOU GUYS LOOKING A--
--WHOA!
WH-WHAT IS THAT...?

IT'S...IT'S MAGIC...
I...I CAN FEEL IT!
AND IT'S NOT GOOD...
...IT'S NOT GOOD AT ALL...
IT'S BAD...
...AND IT KNOWS WE'RE HERE ...!
THRRMMMBLLL
HUH?!
JINKIES!
EVERY-BODY MOVE!

KIDWORLD--

FINALLY ...WE'RE IN!
YEAH, BUT KEEP YOUR EYES OPEN--THE WAY THIS BEDLAM GUY CAN SHIFT AND CHANGE THINGS--WHO KNOWS WHAT WE'RE RACING INTO...?!

WELL, IT LOOKS THE SAME... KINDA ...BUT IT FEELS--
HEY! WHAT'S THAT?
JUSTICE LEAGUE OF AMERICA
OH, THAT'S THE OLD JUSTICE LEAGUE EMBLEM --THEIR SHIELD!

...SHIELD?
JUSTICE LEAGUE OF AMERICA
THAT'S STUPID!

I DON'T KNOW. IT LOOKS THE SAME, BUT I DON'T REMEMBER THE CAVE BEING LAID OUT LIKE THIS WHEN WE WERE HERE WITH THE LEGION OF SUPER HEROES.
I MEAN, WHERE DID ALL THESE EXTRA PASSAGE-WAYS COME FROM ...?
BEDLAM.
HEY, YOU GUYS! COME AND LOOK AT THIS!

IT'S LIKE THIS MUSTA BEEN THE JUSTICE LEAGUE'S OLD STORE ROOM OR TROPHY ROOM OR SOMETHING...!
THERE'S ALL KINDSA COOL STUFF HERE!
WASN'T THIS ROOM ON THE OTHER SIDE OF THE MOUNTAIN ...?
YEAH. EVERYTHING'S ALL TWISTED AROUND ...I DON'T LIKE IT.
I'LL TELL HIM.
EXCUSE ME?! BART?! HEL-LOOO?! WE'RE NOT HERE FOR SIGHT-SEEING... REMEMBER ...?!
...COME ON!
OH... YEAH, RIGHT...
...BEDLAM, ER...
?!
HEY, YOU GUYS--
--WAIT FOR ME!
ZZWIPP

HEY, YOU GUYS --WHERE DIOJA--
ZZAWIPP
--OH.
WHAT ARE YA LOOKING A--
--OH.
ERRT
THERE THEY ARE. THE ORIGINAL JUSTICE LEAGUE.
WOW.
COULD WE EVER BE THAT...?

THIS IS WHACK! WHERE IS THIS BEDLAM GUY...? AND WHY DOES HE HAVE THE CAVE ALL JUMBLED AROUND LIKE SOME KIND OF MAZE?! UNLESS...
UNLESS HE'S STALLING?! UNLESS HE'S NOT READY FOR US YET... OR MAYBE HE'S... AFRAID OF US? WHICH IS WHY WE'VE GOT TO FIND HIM RIGHT NOW...
...AND CATCH HIM BY SURPRISE!
COOL!
GRAMPA.
BART! C'MON!
ZWIPP

EVERYONE SPREAD OUT! THIS PHENOMENON SEEMS TO BE FOCUSING ON US AS A GROUP, TRYING TO PREVENT US FROM GETTING INTO THE CAVE!
WHATEVER'S DOING THIS, WE CAN DIFFUSE ITS STRENGTH IF WE FORCE IT TO DEAL WITH US INDIVIDUALLY!
THAT SEEMS TO BE WOR-- GREAT GOD! THE BOY--!
--BILLY! DON'T--
DON'T SWEAT IT, ZAURIEL --I GOT 'IM!
BILLY, COME BACK HERE! YOU CAN'T--
--WHOA...

"HOLY MOLEY!" IT'S CAPTAIN MARVEL !?!
IN SOME SORT OF... SUSPENDED ANIMATION!
WHAT COULD HAVE...
THERE SEEMS TO BE SOME KIND OF... MAGICAL INTERFERENCE. I'M UNABLE TO REACH MARVEL TELEPATHICALLY...
...BUT PERHAPS, BILLY, IN THAT YOU AND THE CAPTAIN ARE TECHNICALLY THE SAME PERSON, IF I WERE TO USE YOU AS A PSIONIC CONDUIT...
GO AHEAD, MR. J'ONZZ-- I'M KINDA CURIOUS TO KNOW WHAT'S GOING ON HERE MYS--
AND INSTANTLY ...THEY KNOW...
--AS J'ONN J'ONZZ, THE MARTIAN MANHUNTER, USES HIS TELEPATHIC ABILITIES TO LINK THE YOUNG BILLY BATSON TO THE CATATONIC MIND OF HIS ADULT ALTER EGO--

MEMORIES UNFOLD TO THEM, BLOSSOMING LIKE A FLOWER--
AS AN UNAWARE CAPTAIN MARVEL, RETURNING FROM AN EXHAUSTING ADVENTURE IS STUCK AND ENVELOPED IN A VIOLENT VIOLET ENERGY.
IN EXECUTING THE CREATION OF A SEPARATE AND IDENTICAL WORLD, THE OMNIPOTENT BEDLAM REQUIRED A NEXUS THROUGH WHICH TO FOCUS HIS MAGIKS--
--AN UNWITTING INSTRUMEN WITH WHICH TO GIVE FORM THIS NEW REALITY. AN INGENUOUS ID TO GIVE SHAPE TO THIS NEW WORL
--A DREAMER TO DREAM THE DREAM...
THOUGH THE MIGHTIEST MORTAL ON THE PLANET, CAPTAIN MARVEL'S MIND IS STILL THAT OF BILLY BATSON, HIS DREAMS AND FANTASIES THOSE OF A 13-YEAR-OLD BOY.
WHAT BETTER TEMPLATE, THEN, FOR THE JUVENILE GODLING TO USE THAN THE BRIGHT IMAGINATION OF THE MOST CHILD-LIKE OF ADULTS, WHO JUST HAPPENS TO HAVE THE WISDOM OF SOLOMON.
AND ONCE THE LINK IS BROKEN--
IT WOULD APPEAR, MY FRIENDS, THAT WE FACE AN INTERESTING DILEMMA...
OUR YET-UNKNOWN ADVERSARY HAS, THROUGH MAGICAL MEANS, THE POWERS OF A GOD--AND IS RESPONSIBLE FOR THE SPELL THAT NOW BINDS CAPTAIN MARVEL!
AS BATMAN SURMISED BEFORE, THIS EARTH IS NOT OUR OWN, BUT THE MORE TERRIFYING TRUTH IS THAT THIS REALITY IS BEING FUELED BY THE GOOD CAPTAIN'S IMAGINATION--
--THE WORLD WE NOW INHABIT IS CAPTAIN MARVEL'S DREAM!!!
WELL, THEN, IF CAP'S THE ONE WHO'S DREAMING THIS WHOLE EXTRA WORLD... WHY DON'T WE JUST WAKE HIM UP?
WHOA, WHOA, WHOA!
HOLD ON THERE, BABALOOIE... IF WE WAKE THE GUY WHO'S DREAMING OUR REALITY...
...THEN WH-WH-WHAT HAPPENS TO US?!

WOW.
WELL, WONDER BOY--YOU WANTED TO FIND THIS DUDE...?

...I THINK YOU GOT YOUR WISH.
ARE YOU BEDLAM?
I AM BEDLAM... ALTHOUGH I'M GETTING USED TO THE NAME GOD!
AND THAT SHOULD BE TRUE ANY MINUTE NOW, AS MORE AND MORE PEOPLE, KIDS AND GROWN-UPS ALIKE, CONTINUE TO ACCEPT THIS REALITY I'VE CREATED!
JUST BY BELIEVING, THEY'RE MAKING ME INVINCIBLE!
OH, AND I KNOW THAT YOU'RE HERE TO TRY AND STOP ME... SORRY, I'M GONNA HAFTA CRUSH YOU!
YOU'RE BEING SUCH... ADULTS ABOUT THIS...!

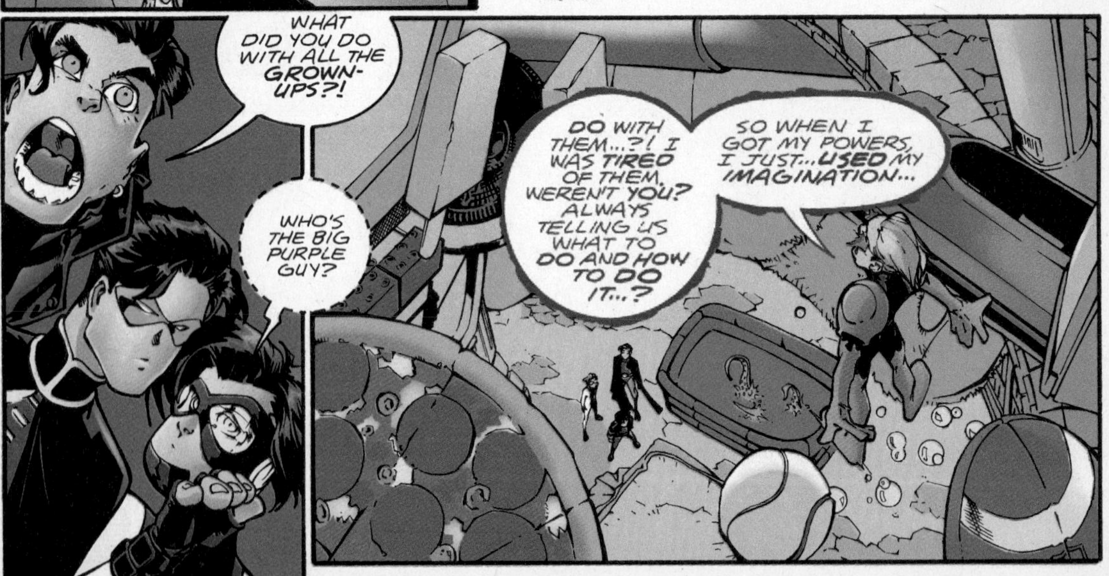
WHAT DID YOU DO WITH ALL THE GROWN-UPS?!
WHO'S THE BIG PURPLE GUY?
DO WITH THEM...?! I WAS TIRED OF THEM, WEREN'T YOU? ALWAYS TELLING US WHAT TO DO AND HOW TO DO IT...?
SO WHEN I GOT MY POWERS, I JUST...USED MY IMAGINATION...

...LIKE THIS!!!

HEY!
SKOOM
SKOOM

AND WHILE I KNOW WHO YOU ARE, I'M NOT SURE THAT I'D BE ABLE TO... IMAGINE ANY WAY TO DEFEAT THE THREE OF YOU... BUT THAT'S OKAY...
...I'M SURE YOU CAN!!!

"YOU SEE, IT WOULD BE... CHILD'S PLAY...

"...FOR ME TO TAP INTO YOUR IMAGI-NATIONS...

"...AND JUST LET YOU DEFEAT EACH OTHER!"
UH OH.

"FOR EXAMPLE, HOW WOULD ROBIN TAKE DOWN SUPERBOY-..?!"
NO! IT'S--
KID! LOOK OUT!
KRA-RUNCH
UNGH!

"...OR WHAT WOULD SUPERBOY DEVISE TO COMPLETELY DESTROY IMPULSE?!"
HUH?!? I-I CAN'T MOVE! CAN'T VIBRATE! CAN'T EVEN MOVE A MUSCLE!
IT... HURTS --STANDING STILL! IT'S DRIVING ME--
S-SORRY, BART...

"...AND WHAT WOULD SPRING FROM IMPULSE'S MIND TO BURY--"
--ROBIN! DUCK! IT'S--

HAHAHA HA! NOW...THIS ...IS COOL! HAHAHA!

THWISH
NINJAS ?!?
THIS IS THE DEAD-LIEST... UM... DEATHTRAP THAT... UH... BART COULD COME UP WITH...? THAT'S IT...?!?
WHAT A LAME...
NO...THAT'S NOT JUST IT! MY THOUGHTS ...THEY'RE ALL... UM, FUZZY!
THWAK
HUH HHN!
THAT BART'S ...MUCH QUICKER THAN I...THOUGHT ...CLOUDED MY MIND...CAN'T THINK...HAVE TO CLEAR MY... HEAD!...
WE ALL DO ...!
SPAKK
YOU GUYS-- QUICK! THINK OF NOTHING!--
--CLEAR YOUR THOUGHTS AND MAYBE ALL THIS STUFF WILL--
--GO AWAY!
TWINK
TWINK
TWINK

HEY, NOT BAD --!
--AND ROBIN ...YOU DA MAN!-- EVEN THOUGH YOUR THOUGHTS WERE ALL MUDDY LIKE THAT, YOU WERE STILL ABLE TO WIN!...
...OR WERE YOU ...?
THE TWO OF YOU HAD ENOUGH FORCE OF WILL TO CLEAR YOUR MINDS COMPLETELY--
--BUT YOUR LITTLE FRIEND OVER THERE...
NOTHING NOTHING NOTHING NOTHING NOTHING NOTHING
NO NO NO NO
NO NO N--
SIGH
SORRY, GUYS--I... I JUST COULDN'T STOP...!
TELL ME AGAIN...? HE'S S'POSED TO BE ON OUR SIDE, RIGHT?

IT'S NOT A MATTER OF WAKING HIM UP...
...BUT OF WHAT YOU'RE WILLING TO BELIEVE!
WHO ?!
WHO ELSE ...?
ALTHOUGH IT'S CAPTAIN MARVEL'S IMAGINATION THAT'S MAINTAINING THIS REALITY--THE DETAILS OF THE "DREAM" WERE PLANTED THERE BY SOMEONE ELSE...
...THEORETICALLY, IF WE WERE TO LINK OUR MINDS VIA J'ONN'S TELEPATHY--APPLYING OUR COMBINED IMAGINATIONS TO INFLUENCE MARVEL'S "DREAM"--
--WE COULD MERGE THE TWO SEPARATE REALITIES BACK TOGETHER.
IT WOULD JUST BE A MATTER OF BELIEVING IT ENOUGH.
AND THIS WOULD WORK?
EITHER THAT, OR WE COULD INADVERTENTLY ERASE THIS REALITY AND ALL OF US WOULD SUDDENLY CEASE TO EXIST.
HE'S JOKING, RIGHT...? TELL ME HE'S JOKING...!
HE DOESN'T JOKE.

HAHAHA
THIS IS GREAT!
UUUN NGH!
POW
OOOF!
WAM
SOK
THERE'S NO WAY I COULD'VE COME UP WITH THIS COOL STUFF!!! AND THE BEST PART IS-- I'M NOT EVEN DOING IT...!
ALL I HAD TO DO WAS GIVE LIFE TO IMPULSE'S THOUGHTS...

...AND THEN JUST KICK BACK WHILE HIS IMAGINATION TOTALLY OBLITERATES HIS BUDDIES!
HAHAHA
KWAMMM
TUDD
HUNFF!

SUPERBOY
ROBIN

SLOW DOWN AND--

--THINK. SLOW DOWN AND THINK. SLOW DOWN AND THINK.
JUST HAFTA CLEAR MY THOUGHTS. I CAN DO THIS. I'M--

IMPULSE!? DO SOME-THING!
SHUNK
SHUNK
WE'RE GETTING KILLED OVER HERE!
YEAH, BART! UNGHFF! AND THIS ISN'T LIKE YOUR STUPID VIDEO GAMES!--
--WE'VE ONLY GOT ONE LIFE EACH!
THAT'S IT!
AND NOW, YOU LITTLE DWEEB, BEFORE YOU GET ANY OTHER BRIGHT IDEAS...
TRY THIS, BEDLAM--
--RESET!!!

?!
FWINK
FWINK
HEY...IT WORKED!
FWINK
WHOA!
EVERY-THING DIS-APPEARED! WE CAN--

BIG DEAL! I STILL HAVE THE POWER! I CAN JUST AS EASILY--
RESET.
...
CUT THAT OUT OR I'LL--
RESET. RESET. RESET.

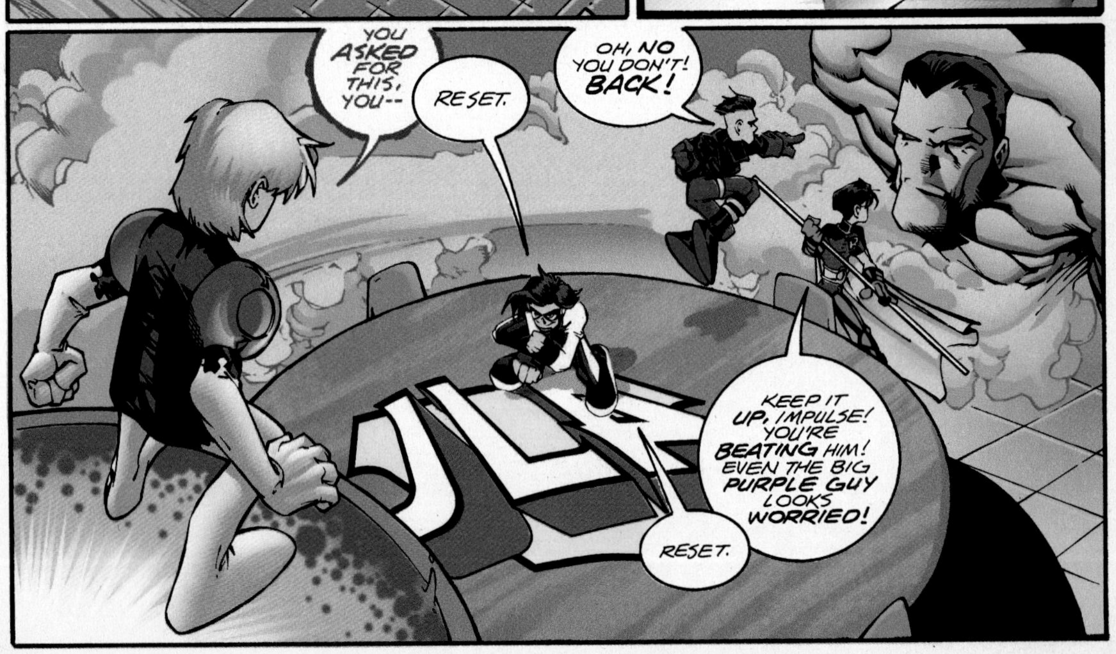
YOU ASKED FOR THIS, YOU--
RESET.
OH, NO YOU DON'T! BACK!
KEEP IT UP, IMPULSE! YOU'RE BEATING HIM! EVEN THE BIG PURPLE GUY LOOKS WORRIED!
RESET.

YOU JERK! I'LL--
RESET.
I'M GONNA--
RESET.
THAT'S IT, BART! KEEP 'IM COVERED!
YOU'VE GOT HIM OFF BALANCE! HE'S LOSING HIS FOCUS...
...AND HIS CONFIDENCE!
NO! NO! YOU CAN'T BEAT ME! I'M INVINCIBLE! I HAVE THE POWER TO DESTROY YOU! I HAVE THE POWER OF A--
--GOD!

HEY, YOU GUYS...IT'S WORKING! THE PURPLE GUY IS SHRINKING!
YOU'RE NOT A GOD, BEDLAM-- A GOD NEEDS PEOPLE TO BELIEVE IN HIM...AND YOU DON'T EVEN BELIEVE IN YOURSELF!
YOU'RE JUST A KID WHO GOT SOME POWERS...
NO... I...

--POWERS THAT WEREN'T EVEN YOURS TO HAVE...
I WAS...

HEADS UP, EVERYBODY! THE DEFENSE SYSTEM'S PICKED UP AN ENERGY SIGNATURE IN THE WESTERN QUADRANT, AND IT'S COMING IN FAST!
WEST?! WE'RE ON THE MOON! WHICH WAY IS--
HEY! I MADE IT IN... I...
GOTCHA, YA LITTLE MONKEY!
OH, YOU MAY LOOK LIKE A REGULAR LITTLE KID, BUT WE GOT YOUR NUMBER...
PLAS!?! I'VE GOT HIM! GET OUT OF THERE! YOU'RE GONNA--
HEY !?!
SKRAKKLE

ENOUGH, YOU TWO! LANTERN, REMOVE THE CAGE--
--THIS IS BILLY BATSON!
THANKS, MARTIAN MANHUNTER!
...BILLY BATSON?
EXCUSE US, PLEASE.
BILLY--WHAT ARE YOU DOING HERE? AND MAYBE MORE IMPORTANT...
...WHERE IS CAPTAIN MARVEL?
AND SO HE TELLS THEM, THESE SELECT FEW WHO KNOW OF HIS DUALITY, HOW HE WOKE UP THIS MORNING TO A WORLD WITHOUT GROWN-UPS...
HOW HE CONTINUED WITH HIS JOB AT WHIZ, CONCERNED ABOUT WHERE THE ADULTS HAD DISAPPEARED TO, HESITANT TO SPEAK HIS MAGIC WORD FOR FEAR THAT HE WOULD DO THE SAME!
HOW HE HAD BEEN VISITED BY ROBIN, SUPERBOY, AND IMPULSE, AND WAS RELUCTANT TO BECOME CAPTAIN MARVEL AT ROBIN'S REQUEST...
...BUT LATER FOUND THE COURAGE DEEP INSIDE HIM TO TAKE THE LEAP, TO SPEAK THE WORD...

AND YET, YOU WERE TRANSPORTED HERE, BUT NOT TRANS-FORMED INTO CAPTAIN MARVEL...?!
YEAH. THAT'S WEIRD...
...I SAID THE MAGIC WORD, I CAME TO THE ADULT-WORLD, SO WHY DIDN'T I BECOME CAP? IF I'M BILLY BATSON HERE...
THEN WHERE IS CAPTAIN MARVEL?
ANYWAY, WHEN I WAS BE-TWEEN THE TWO WORLDS, I COULD SEE THEM BOTH CON-NECTED BY THIS STRANGE PURPLE ENERGY THAT LOOKED LIKE IT WAS COMING FROM SOMEPLACE ON THE EAST COAST...
...THE GUYS WERE GOING THERE TO CHECK IT OUT-- SOMEPLACE CALLED--
--HAPPY HARBOR!
WHAT ARE THEY TALKING ABOUT?
HAPPY HARBOR.
HAPPY HARBOR ...?
SOUNDS LIKE A RETIREMENT HOME!
DOES THAT MEAN ANY-THING?
WHAT DID I SAY?
I HAVEN'T GOT A CLUE, BUT IT SURE MEANT SOMETHING TO THEM!

YOU ARE NOW
ENTERING TO
KIDWORLD--
HEY, YOU GUYS-- IS IT JUST ME...
...OR ARE WE, LIKE, NOT GETTING ANY CLOSER...?
BEDLAM
NO SHIRT SHOES PROBLEM
NO ID REQUIRED
I MEAN, I CAN SEE THE ENTRANCE, BUT EVERY TIME I TRY TO GET THERE... I DON'T!? WHAT'S UP WITH THAT!?
IT'S LIKE... THE CLOSER WE GET, THE FARTHER AWAY WE ARE!
THIS WAY
WAIT A MINUTE... LET'S FOCUS ON WHAT WE KNOW.
WE DON'T KNOW WHO'S RESPONSIBLE FOR ALL THIS, BUT WE DO KNOW THAT THEY'VE GOTTA BE PRETTY POWERFUL TO'VE MADE ALL THE ADULTS DISAPPEAR! THEY MUST HAVE THE POWER TO AT LEAST BEND REALITY...
HOW ELSE TO EXPLAIN THE OLD JUSTICE LEAGUE HEADQUARTERS AND SURROUNDING LANDSCAPE LOOKING LIKE SOME KINDA TWISTED TIM BURTON CARTOON ...?!
...BENDING REALITY...? GREAT--
--HOW DO YOU FIGHT THAT?
NO ...HOW DO YOU FIGHT--
--THAT ?!?
WHRRRR
THIP-THIP
RUMMBL

WHAT IS IT?!
I DON'T KNOW. BE READY.
RUMMBLE
GANG-WAY! COMING THROUGH!
?
UP, UP, AND AWAY!
?
JUSTICE WILL BE SERVED!
?
HEY, WATCH IT!
GET OFF MY TAIL!
JUSTA LOTTA ANIMALS COMIN' THROUGH!

I THINK...
I THINK I DID THAT... I MEAN, MY THOUGHTS...
...'CAUSE I WAS JUST THINKING ABOUT THE JUSTICE LEAGUE, AND...
...AND CARTOONS...

ARE THEY READING OUR THOUGHTS?
HUH?!

OH, THAT'S JUST GREAT! SOMEONE WHO CAN ALTER REALITY AND READ YOUR MIND! WE ARE GONNA GET SO SPANKED!

SOMEONE WITH THAT KINDA POWER...!?!... WE'RE DONE! I MEAN...THAT'S LIKE, IMAGINE YOUR WORSTEST POSSIBLE VILLAIN, AND--

FWINK
FWINK
FWINK

SOMEWHERE...
ME AND MY BIG MOUTH! SOMEONE WHO CAN READ MINDS AND ALTER REALITY, AND I HAVE TO GO AND GIVE THEM IDEAS!? GOOD GOIN', KID!
NOW, IF I CAN ONLY FIND OUT WHERE I AM AND HOW TO GET BACK TO THE OTHER GUYS...!
HELLO, MEAT! I WAS WONDERING WHEN YOU'D SHOW UP!
I'VE ALWAYS WANTED A PIECE OF THE LITTLE SUPER-CLONE-- I COULD JUST NEVER DECIDE WHICH PIECE...!
METALLO!
...OR AT LEAST SOME FREAKY KID VERSION OF HIM!
WELL, HERE'S THE PUNCH-LINE, METAL-HEAD--
--BEFORE THAT KRYPTONITE HEART OF YOURS CAN AFFECT ME!
KRANG
KRAK
KRAK
KRAMM
OH, YOU'VE GOT ME CONFUSED WITH THE ORIGINAL, BRAT--I'M THE SEQUEL!
I DON'T JUST CARRY KRYPTONITE--
--I AM KRYPTONITE!
UNGH!
POW
HASTA LA PASTA--
--BABEEE!

SOMEWHERE ...ELSE--
WHOA! WHERE AM I?
SUPERBOY SAID "THINK OF THE WORSTEST VILLAIN," AND I--
are you READY, whelp--
HUH?!
...over HERE!
--to face the thundering might of... GRODD !?!
GRODD?! BUT YOU'RE A--
YOU WERE EXPECTING SOMETHING...
...BIGGER?!
YIPE!
RUN, LITTLE HUMAN--YOU CANNOT ESCAPE ME!
HERE, GRODD IS FASTER! STRONGER--
--UGLIER!

KEEP IT UP, ROB-- HE'S GOING...
...AND THE ONLY THING THOSE POWERS GOT YOU WAS TROUBLE...
ALL I WANTED WAS FOR EVERY-THING...

...FEEL THAT? I THINK IT'S WORKING!
...GOING...
BUT NOW YOU'RE TIRED OF THOSE POWERS AND ALL THAT TROUBLE AND CONFUSION, AREN'T YOU? AND YOU JUST WISH THAT EVERYTHING WAS BACK TO NORMAL...
...AND THAT YOU COULD JUST GO TO SLEEP...
YEAH...I ...SLEEP...? I COULD...

ROBIN--
IMPULSE--
-PERBOY
WHAT...
...HE'S OUTTA HERE!
...SO GO AHEAD ...IT'S OKAY... GO TO SLEEP...
QUIET, THEY'RE--
...SLEEP...

-XCELLENT!
INCREDIBLE!
THEY DID IT!
-SO COOL!
HEY, WHERE'D THEY COME FROM?

SOME TIME LATER--
SO YOU'RE SAYING THAT THE BOY WILL STAY IN YOUR CARE...?
UNTIL WE CAN ASSESS THE EXTENT--
--AND POTENTIAL THREAT--OF HIS ABILITIES.
--CURRENT STATE OF CATATONIA--
--PROUD OF YOU, BART!
THANKS, MAX...
...AM I STILL GROUNDED...?
ORACLE REPORTS THAT EVERYTHING IS BACK TO NORMAL. THE ENTIRE JUSTICE LEAGUE WAS... STUMPED.
YOU AND YOUR FRIENDS DID A... FINE JOB, ROBIN.
UM... YEAH...
...THANKS.
COME ON. IT'S A LONG DRIVE BACK TO GOTHAM.

HEY, WONDER --WHERE YA GOIN'?
OH, UH...
...GOTTA GO...
SEE YA.
WHAT ARE YOU STOPPING FOR?
ROBIN...
TIM...
YOU, SUPERBOY, AND IMPULSE DID AN EXCELLENT JOB BACK THERE...
AND...
...AND I'M PROUD OF YOU.
AND...
WHAT?!
I'LL SEE YOU BACK IN GOTHAM.
WOW.

ROBIN ...?!
HEY, BATMAN SAID I COULD STICK AROUND AND YOU WANNA KNOW SOME-THING...
YOU TWO MIGHT THINK WE DID PRETTY GOOD OUT THERE, THAT WE ACTED LIKE A TEAM, WORKED WELL TOGETHER... THAT MAYBE-- SOMEDAY-- WE ACTUALLY COULD TAKE OVER FOR THE JLA...?
WELL, LET ME TELL YOU SOMETHING... AS THE JUNIOR JUSTICE LEAGUE...
...WE SERIOUSLY ROCK!!!
ALL RIIIGHT!
SWEET!... ALTHOUGH WE GOTTA COME UP WITH SOMETHING BETTER THAN JUSTICE LEAGUE JUNIOR... THAT JUST HURTS!
WITH A LITTLE PRACTICE, WE COULD DO SOME GREAT THINGS!
NOW, C'MON, PARTNERS! LET'S GET BACK TO THE PARTY! I LOVE TO HEAR WONDER WOMAN TELL ME WHAT A GREAT JOB WE DID...!
YEAH, THAT IS KINDA COOL, ISN'T IT...?
YEAH. JUST REMEMBER NOT TO LOOK AT HER "EAGLE" WHEN SHE'S TALKING TO YA...
I DON'T GET IT... WHADDAYA TALKIN' ABOUT?
FERGET IT, BART... I'LL EXPLAIN IT TO YA LATER...
THE END...?

RAMOS/FAUCHER

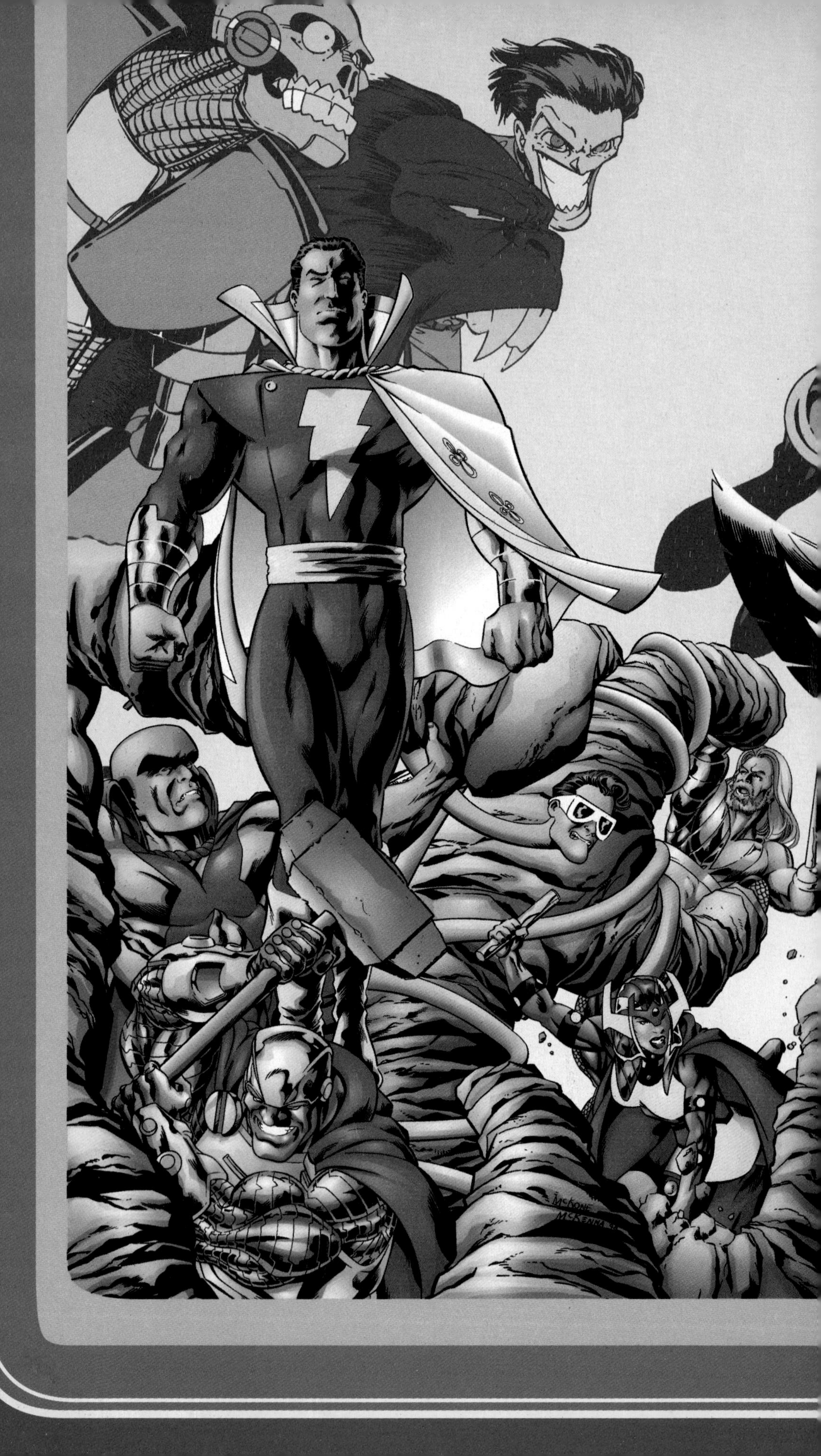
McKONE
McKENNA